Choices

Materials and methods for Personal and Social Education

David Settle and Charles Wise

Basil Blackwell

This publication is based on the television series *Choices* produced by Central Independent Television plc.

Central logo copyright © 1982
Central Independent Television plc

© David Settle and Charles Wise 1986
First published 1986

Published by Basil Blackwell Ltd
108 Cowley Road
Oxford OX4 1JF
England

British Library Cataloguing in Publication Data

Settle, David
   Choices: materials and methods for
   personal and social education.
   1. Life skills—Study and teaching
   (Secondary)—Great Britain
   I. Title   II. Wise, Charles
   370.11′5′0941   HQ2039.G7

   ISBN 0–631–90129–9

Typeset in 11 on 13pt Plantin
by Katerprint Typesetting Services, Oxford
Printed in Great Britain by T.J. Press (Padstow) Ltd

Contents

The titles of the Central television programmes in the *Choices* series which may be used in association with specific chapters are as follows:

Chapter	Programme title
3	Who am I?
4	Changes
5	How others see us
6	Practically perfect
7	Food for thought
8	A right Charlie
9	Being happy is what matters most
10	Dear Sally
11	Helping each other
12	Looking forward

Further information about the television films may be obtained from the Education Officer at your local ITV company.

For Adam, Catherine, Daniel, Samantha and Steven

Acknowledgements

We would like to record our sincere thanks to all those colleagues and friends who have advised and supported us throughout the preparation of this book.

For their comments on drafts of the chapters and their suggestions about the way the materials should be presented, we owe a great debt of gratitude to Sylvia Winchester and Susan Wise. To Hazel Brook and Linda Settle, we offer our special thanks for typing several drafts with great speed, accuracy and patience.

To our friends at Central television, especially Philip Grosset, Paul Davies and Dirk Campbell, we thank them for their encouragement and sustained interest, and for involving us in an advisory capacity in the Schools Television series 'Choices'.

Introduction

In May 1985, we were invited by Central Television to act as advisers for the production of *Choices*, a ten-programme schools television series designed for pupils aged 11 and over. The series was primarily intended to support Personal and Social Education courses. As advisers we were asked to produce a teacher's booklet of activities and ideas to support each of the programmes. Following research among pupils of this age group and discussions with teachers we felt that a more detailed book would provide a valuable resource and so this book came to be written.

We hope that the book will provide interesting ideas and examples for teachers who may not view the series but who are seeking more activities, materials and methods for use in personal and social education courses. Even if a reader does not wish to use the programme topics, he may wish to consider the philosophy which underpins the various approaches and processes.

Although attention has been paid to the developmental nature of the activities within any one programme, they should not be viewed as a 'series of hoops' through which to jump; there is scope for teachers and pupils to develop their own resources from any stimulus provided in the book.

In chapter 1, we consider the notion of 'choice' and how it is related to the methods which are used with young people to examine decision-making in different social contexts. Some assumptions about the relative merits of didactic and less-didactic approaches are examined from the perspective of both the teacher and the pupil. Having thus outlined our viewpoint on the process of schooling and its relationship to academic and social learning, we then suggest that less-didactic teaching approaches have the potential to offer pupils opportunities to consider and exercise choice for themselves, irrespective of the content or topic under consideration.

In advocating that pupils be given greater responsibility for their own and each others' learning, we are not recommending an abdication, but rather a re-definition, of the teacher's responsibility. It requires equal, if not greater, skill and sensitivity to 'take a step back' – to provide young people with space, time and support as they examine and reconsider together their experience and perceptions of the world.

Chapter 2 is devoted to the issues raised by the use of small group work as a major feature of less didactic approaches. Many factors combine in various ways to influence the learning outcomes of small group work: group size and composition; the nature and duration of the task; the learning environment; the role of the teacher; and the roles within groups. In this chapter, for the purpose of analysis, each feature is dealt with individually in order to sharpen the focus upon the demands of small group work on teacher and learner.

Chapters 3 to 12 contain activities related to the content of each of the 15 minute television programmes, although they can equally well be used independently. It is essential for teachers to read the description of each activity with a particular group of pupils in mind and consider its feasibility and suitability, *prior to* its use in any learning situation.

Wherever possible, we have suggested a time-scale for each task within an activity. However, different classes and groups will vary in the amount of time they spend on the tasks, so in some cases we leave this to the teacher to decide.

While the methods of working described here have been used with young people in many and varied educational contexts it is clearly impossible to compile activities that will be appropriate to the needs, interests, rights and responsibilities of every individual and group within a multi-cultural society. The teacher will wish, therefore, to modify, amend, and adapt the activities to take account of their own particular circumstances and needs.

Throughout the book we have used 'he' for consistency of style, but we recognise that this reference could equally well be 'she'.

David Settle
Charles Wise
July 1986

1 Choices and the promotion of learning

A notion of 'choice'

Every day each individual makes hundreds of choices, some of them are mundane and routine, others are profound and significant. The idea that we act as free agents in making such choices may be a fantasy; we may be influenced by a range of apparent and hidden factors, such as the actual or perceived behaviour of other people; the social context; our own attitudes, beliefs, values, knowledge and skills; the media; legislation; religion; socio-economic circumstances; even climatic conditions. Any combination of these may influence how we exercise choice.

In this book, we aim to offer choice to teachers and pupils through a range of suggested activities, and to encourage either or both parties to develop their own agenda. The contents do not represent a course but, within each chapter, the activities have been designed to provide a developmental approach.

The teacher is encouraged to involve pupils in activities that focus upon the way in which choice is exercised. For example, through the use of a set of continua an individual may locate and reflect upon where he stands on various aspects of the decision-making process (Fig. 1.a).

The arrows indicate the possible response of an individual. The location of the arrows is not important; what matters is the opportunity for reflection the continuum provides. This scheme may be used as a private or shared process, with the adaptation or addition of continua. Thus the *process* itself, as well as subsequent actions or outcomes, is an integral part of social learning.

By recognising the multi-dimensional nature of making choices, teachers can offer learning experiences which clarify the meanings of

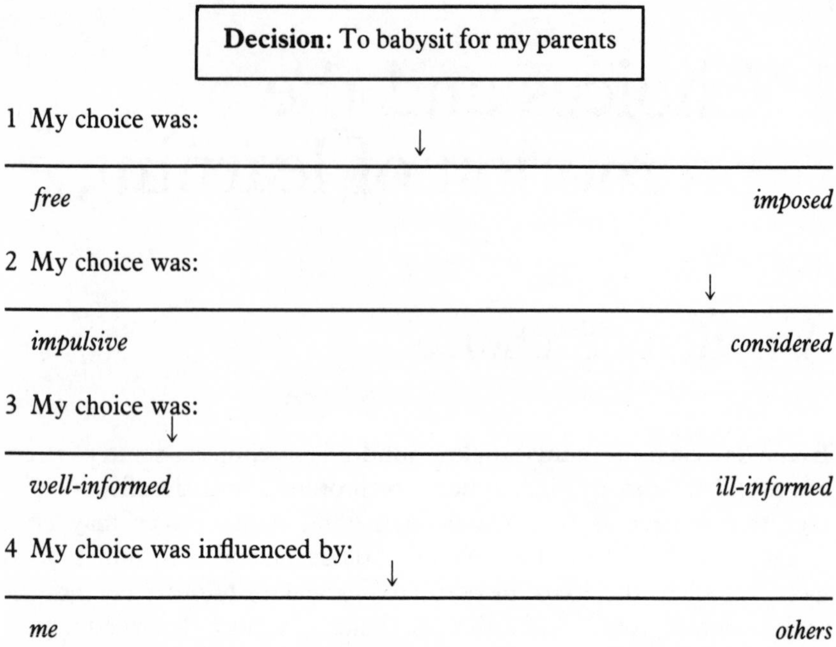

Decision: To babysit for my parents

---

1 My choice was:

$\downarrow$

free   *imposed*

2 My choice was:

$\downarrow$

impulsive   *considered*

3 My choice was:

$\downarrow$

well-informed   *ill-informed*

4 My choice was influenced by:

$\downarrow$

me   *others*

Fig. 1.a Using a set of continua

such terms as 'informed decision-making', 'personal autonomy' and 'self-empowerment'. Furthermore, a pupil may build up a personal or group profile of the occasions when he behaves in a *proactive* way (ie makes things happen) and in a *reactive* way (ie allows things to happen).

A challenge to the schooling experience

In the last ten years there has been a growing interest in the development of teaching methods that provide first-hand learning experiences for pupils, by direct participation. These methods are not new, but their application in secondary schools has been limited. Recently, the focus of attention has been on active learning, developed largely from the work of individuals and organisations such as the Counselling and Career Development Unit in Leeds; Douglas Hamblin in Swansea; and Leslie Button's Developmental Group Work methods which, together with the work of Jill Baldwin and the Active Tutorial Work team (financed by the Health Education Council), have had a significant national impact.

Recently the term 'student-centred learning' has come to the fore, largely through its appearance in many of the Technical and Vocational Education Initiatives (TVEI). One by-product of the Birmingham TVEI scheme has been the publication of *A Guide to Student Centred Learning* by Donna Brandes and Paul Ginnis (Blackwell, 1986), and the reader is directed to the book for a detailed development of this way of working. Recently, student-centred learning has also appeared as a component of the national guidelines for the TVEI related in-service training scheme (TRIST).

The materials in this book lend themselves to styles of teaching that require pupils to be fully participative in the learning process. However we recognise that this process is controlled by the teacher. If the process is to be fully student-centred, the teacher must recognise that young people are themselves the content of their personal and social experience and that the teacher's role is to facilitate effective interactions of pupils.

The use of continua to illustrate choices has already been described. In Figure 1.b continua are used to provide a rough framework indicating the features of didactic and student-centred teaching styles. They offer a set of prompts for reflection on which an analysis of personal styles of teaching can be based.

For the purpose of this book, the distinction drawn between student-centred learning and active learning is that the latter does not create opportunities for learners to take responsibility for their own learning. Teaching for active learning which still involves the teacher in a major controlling role is described here as less didactic teaching. The mere presence of activity and pupil participation should not be confused with student-centred work.

In some schools, pupils' predominant learning experience is as recipients of instruction selected and presented by teachers. They have little opportunity to interact with their peers in the learning process and are expected only to respond to teacher-initiated questions. Thus their opportunities to consider and exercise choice within the curriculum are limited.

Fig. 1.b Didactic vs student-centred teaching styles

DIDACTIC	STUDENT-CENTRED
pupil/pupil talk discouraged	pupil/pupil talk encouraged
pupil/pupil talk controlled by teacher	pupil talk controlled by pupils
pupil movement in the classroom discouraged	pupil movement in in the classroom encouraged
content controlled by teacher	content negotiated with pupils
pupil achievement only assessed by teacher	pupil achievement also assessed by pupil
rules of conduct set and maintained by teacher	rules of conduct set and maintained with teacher
materials produced only by teacher	materials produced with teacher
classroom talk mainly excludes feelings	classroom talk often includes feelings
low level of display of pupils' work	high level of display of pupils' work

display of pupils' work
organised by teacher

display of pupils' work
organised by pupils

talking and listening
skills underdeveloped

talking and listening
skills well developed

pupils seldom required
to think and talk about
what they are learning

pupils often required
to think and talk about
what they are learning

lessons start from
teacher's view of what
pupils already know

lessons start from
pupils describing what
they already know

learning resources
managed by teacher

learning resources
managed with teacher

teacher largely static
in classroom

teacher predominantly
mobile in classroom

If one accepts Douglas' (1983) view that 'Choices can only be made if an awareness of alternatives and their values exists at the moment of decision making. Some choice almost always exists.' then the use of a didactic teaching approach may not be compatible with the notion of choices. Therefore we wish to challenge certain assumptions and to suggest that the way in which pupils work with each other and with teachers may have an important bearing upon their personal and social development.

1 Academic and social learning is fostered by pupil interaction

In the early years of pre-school and primary education, great emphasis is placed upon the importance of peer interaction. Children are encouraged to cooperate, share and participate in each other's learning experiences and to this end, communication is highly valued. However, as young people progress through their secondary school careers, there is a tendency for them to be discouraged from collaborating with members of their group in the classroom. Yet if one observes young people in more informal settings, there is every indication that they wish to interact with each other. The assumption underlying the restriction of peer interaction may be that the only valid learning experience in school is the product of the transaction between teacher and pupil where the former controls the terms of mediation and also its content, extent and style. Such comments as 'I want *your* work, not your friend's' and 'You are here to work, not to talk' are indicative of this assumption.

We do not contend, however, that silence should disappear from the classroom; individual enquiry and study has an important part to play in the development of a flexible range of effective working habits.

2 Schooling should be more concerned with the 'here and now' experience

While we recognise that it is essential to prepare young people for the future, there is a danger that this concentration on an unknown and unpredictable future may be at the expense of adequate consideration of the quality of the day-to-day experience of pupils in our schools.

Arguably, the quality of the experience which the pupil currently enjoys will influence his ability and inclination to retain and develop his role as a 'learner' throughout life. We are convinced that the *way* in which the pupil learns today will be as significant in later life as *what* he learns today.

3 A variety of teaching styles is in the best interest of young people

The view that the teacher is the 'fountain of all knowledge' may not only be inappropriate but positively harmful to the healthy development of young people. Cole (1972) highlights the potent negative influence that a teacher who adopts an exclusively instructive approach may exert upon his pupils.

> Teacher, teacher tell me true
> Tell me what I ought to do!
>
> Teacher, teacher, where's my book?
> Tell me where I ought to look!
>
> Tell me what to feel and how to think,
> When to eat and what to drink.
>
> Tell me what is good and what is bad,
> When I'm happy and when I'm sad.
>
> Tell me, tell me what to do,
> Tell me, tell me what is true.
>
> Make me learn and make me know,
> Watch me closely as I come and go.
>
> For I am small and I am weak,
> Without your permission I cannot speak.
>
> I cannot learn except by your decree,
> Please, I beg you, give knowledge to me.
>
> I am stupid and you are bright,
> I am wrong and you are right.
>
> I am bad and you are good.
> I must do what you say I should.
>
> Oh teacher, teacher, can't you see!
> Look, at what you've done to me!

One of the major potential hazards of 'telling' pupils what they should know, feel and do, is to undervalue their current status and experience and to undermine their self-esteem. The opportunity for pupils to reflect upon and respond to a learning stimulus is a crucial part of the educative process, not a luxury to be offered only if time permits. Without this process of reflection pupils find it difficult to turn experience into learning.

If in their early years of secondary school pupils are expected to be passive recipients of knowledge and prescribed skills, they may not be inclined or equipped to rekindle their enthusiasm for more interactive learning opportunities at later stages when the ability to collaborate and take responsibility will be essential to their development.

4 A 'wrong' answer has a place in the learning process

The major emphasis in the latter years of secondary education tends to be on preparing pupils for external examinations. This can lead to a preoccupation with the measurement of knowledge recall and may seem to suggest that the attainment of the 'right' answer is of paramount importance. Furthermore, this emphasis on 'correctness' may encourage young people to believe that for every problem there is only one right answer. This simplistic view is belied in almost any social context; no two people are likely to respond to a similar situation in an identical manner. This is one aspect of the real world which young people are already encountering. They need to be given opportunities, in a safe and supportive environment, to learn how to handle such situations constructively.

5 A pupil's experience is as important as that of the teacher

Each group member, irrespective of – perhaps because of – ability, age, cultural background, gender or socio-economic situation, is likely to have experiences that may be considered to be 'unique' and specifically relevant to that member's learning needs. As Laing (1967) has said: 'I cannot experience your experience. You cannot experience mine.' In one respect, this statement may suggest that an individual's personal experiences are inaccessible to others. But one of the most significant challenges facing the teacher is how to provide a trusting environment in which a young person feels safe to articulate his interpretation of an experience in the interest of his own and others' personal growth. Young people may be able to offer first-hand experience of a situation of which the teacher has little or no direct knowledge, such as having an unemployed or disabled parent, life in rented accommodation or major responsibilities for rearing their siblings. To harness this experience would be to provide a rich learning resource with greater immediacy and relevance than a visiting speaker's lecture on 'unemployment', 'parenthood', 'the disabled', 'homemaking', 'rights and responsibilities', 'housing in the eighties'! Greater awareness and insight can develop from sharing and discussing pupils' own experiences.

6 The pupil's private and public world requires as much respect as that of the teacher

Although one may wish to use the experience of group members, one should also be mindful of the vulnerability of those who are to be encouraged to participate in self-disclosure activities. At the outset, the teacher should respect the private world of each of the group members: similarly, he should not take advantage of his seniority and burden the group with personal anecdotes or disclosures more appropriate to his own peer group. It is important for teachers and pupils to have a clear understanding of the right of each individual to maintain boundaries between private and public life. This may be represented diagramatically (Fig. 1.c)

		Teacher's world	
		Public	Private
Pupil's world	Public	1	2
	Private	3	4

Fig. 1.c

In the early stages of a group's life, it is important to establish the ground rules by which members will operate. It may be useful for the teacher to explain Figure 1.c and to illustrate what issues may fall within one or more areas; this activity may be developed by the pupils, so that they establish boundaries appropriate to their personal needs. For the teacher embarking upon social education within the formal curriculum it may be most appropriate to begin within the boundaries of area 1. Area 4, in particular, does not seem to be appropriate for pupil-teacher interaction within the classroom. The teacher who sees himself as 'one of the boys' may in fact be encroaching on the private world of the pupils, their families and members of a wider community – and may do so at his own peril!

In the light of the preceding information it is our main thesis that *non-didactic teaching approaches have the potential to offer pupils opportunities to consider and exercise choice irrespective of the content or topic area under consideration.*

Some perspectives on less-didactic approaches

So many constraints and variables influence choice of teaching method that one may conclude that no one way is the *only* way. However, in any specific context some methods are likely to be better than others for the presentation of specific learning opportunities. The most effective teacher has a full range of styles from which to choose according to his professional judgement in varying teaching/learning contexts.

We believe that less-didactic approaches have important advantages, especially when based on small group work. At this stage it might be appropriate to consider teacher and pupil perceptions of what these are and what disadvantages exist. To this end we asked some teachers to make comments on the relative merits and demerits of the approach. We have selected statements that appear to offer the reader a distinctive perspective but we recognise that there are links and overlaps.

Advantages

There is a greater opportunity for each pupil to make a contribution.

Pupils are more likely to contribute in a small group setting than in front of a whole class; there is less likelihood that a particular viewpoint will be exposed to public ridicule.

Pupils feel valued if they have the opportunity to make regular contributions.

A shy person may be encouraged to contribute to a small group task.

The group provides a smaller, more secure working environment.

Few pupils enjoy working alone in silence for most of the school day.

The group may offer support to its members beyond the particular lesson.

Pupils are encouraged to communicate with each other and share opinions and knowledge.

Pupil experience is readily accessible to group members.

Group decisions may be more appropriate and/or informed than individual ones.

Pupil talk is not continually exposed to teacher scrutiny.

Pupils are not under pressure to provide the 'right answer' to questions posed by the teacher.

Completion of the group task is not solely dependent upon the direction of the teacher.

Each group may work in its own way and produce a unique outcome in terms of individual learning and group decision.

The teacher's role may be to act as an enabler rather than the disseminator of factual information.

Certain aims and objectives may only be realised through the use of small group work.

Even though these views indicate an enthusiasm for this way of working, by those who have tried it, the approach is not widely used and accepted in the secondary school. With the emergence of such educational initiatives as CPVE, GCSE and TVEI, schools are gradually investing more time and attention in finding ways of working effectively with young people, and the potential of more interactive approaches is beginning to be appreciated.

Disadvantages
There remains resistance to 'new' methods and loyalty to a more formal and traditional approach. Teachers described the following disadvantages of using less-didactic teaching approaches:

The teacher has not been trained to work in this way.

The teacher may lose control of the class; one's colleagues may object to the noise created in an adjoining room.

Only charismatic teachers are capable of using group work.

The amount of time invested in preparation is disproportionate to the number of occasions in a week when the teacher has the opportunity to use group work.

Pupils may not value this approach as it is alien to their common day-to-day experience in school; this view may be shared by other colleagues, governors and parents.

The teacher may not 'get through the syllabus' if this approach is used.

There are no readily available criteria for the objective measurement of learning outcomes.

There is the fear that pupils may become engaged in the discussion about sensitive issues which cause embarrassment to other group members and, perhaps, to the teacher.

The school's senior management team may view the activities as 'play rather than work'.

It is difficult to know how long to let activities run.

Pupils may refuse to participate.

It is impossible to accommodate the most and the least articulate within the class.

The use of less-didactic approaches can only be justified in classes which are not preparing for external examinations.

Once a group activity has been completed it is difficult for pupils to describe what they've learned.

This approach provides an ideal opportunity for pupils to engage in disruptive behaviour.

Children have plenty of time out of school to talk with their friends and hang around in groups.

The pupils' perspective
During our research we also asked pupils who had worked in this way to comment upon the advantages they had perceived. They expressed

enthusiasm for their new-found role; the group work experience was highly valued because, they claimed, it gave them the opportunity to:

1 develop their own agenda;
2 take responsibility for group decisions;
3 engage in discussion as an aid to learning;
4 experience a wide range of materials, media and methods;
5 initiate their own enquiries;
6 'use' the teacher as a resource, rather than as an expert and judge;
7 move about within the classroom, school and community during the working day;
8 reflect upon their learning and current state of knowledge;
9 use their knowledge as a baseline for developmental work;
10 devise an agreed 'division of labour' with the group for a range of activities and tasks;
11 engage in cooperative and collaborative rather than competitive activities;
12 formulate ways of evaluating *their* learning;
13 take responsibility for creating and collating their own learning resources;
14 support group members who were experiencing difficulties (both within and outside school);
15 listen to each other rather than only to the teacher;
16 learn from each other.

Some pupils did not feel so positive; they expressed the view that:

> *'It's boring.'*
> *'It's a waste of time.'*
> *'It's not real work.'*
> *'The teacher has a rest.'*
> *'It's too much like hard work.'*
> *'I can't see any point in it.'*
> *'We just sit around and chat.'*

However, there was some indication that these pupils felt disenchanted with school life in general. Their negative reactions, therefore, may not reflect solely a rejection of this particular way of working.

These varied responses raise too many issues to be fully developed here. Nevertheless they do indicate the potential depth and richness of group experience for young people. In Chapter 2 we will consider some of the main issues involved in adopting such an approach.

References

Brandes, D. and Ginnis, P. *A guide to student-centred learning*: Oxford: Basil Blackwell, 1986

Cole, H. *Tell me, teacher* handout at Creative Problem Solving Institute, Creative Education Foundation, Buffalo, New York State, 1972

Douglas, T. *Groups: Understanding people gathered together* London: Tavistock Publications, 1983

Laing, R. D. *The politics of experience* Harmondsworth: Penguin, 1967

2 Working with groups

The teaching described in this book emphasises group work. Group work is not the only way to teach, neither is it the best way to teach. There is no one best way to teach. The effective teacher employs a range of teaching styles in response to learners' needs, attempting to get a good match between the intended learning outcomes, pupils' perceived and described needs and the process of learning being facilitated.

So why emphasise learning in groups? We would identify three major reasons. First, in the majority of secondary schools the emphasis is generally on didactic processes directed towards the whole class, as if the individuals within it were all at the same starting point, with the same motivation and intentions – which is clearly not the case. Second, the didactic approach takes no account of the capacity of young people to work together and support each other. We believe that working in small support groups should be a major part of the learner's experience of school. Third, there is also a predominance of teacher-pupil interactions in didactic class teaching. In criticising this, we do not condone a laissez-faire approach, based on uncontrolled pupil-pupil interactions. Rather we wish to acknowledge that most learners live in the world of their peer group. To underestimate, on the one hand, the limitations this can impose on personal achievement, or, on the other, to undervalue its immense potential for personal support, is to risk neglecting a crucial area of pupils' experience as it relates to life beyond school.

There is a natural tendency in most pupils – and, indeed, in most adults – to want to talk together. Through talking we rehearse and release our ideas, test out other people's reactions and modify our thinking, values, behaviours and attitudes accordingly. The Personal and Social Education curriculum is about values, behaviour and attitudes as well as knowledge and skills. We therefore need to foster pupil talk. But we must do this in a creative, interesting and lively way, using the pupils themselves as the major resource. In effect, pupils are the content of this curriculum; the context is largely their groups. Not to work in groups is to put at risk elements of personal achievement. We cannot experience groups and their influences on us other than *in* groups.

Schooling is based upon groupings. In some cases, groupings may be formed to segregate and discriminate between individuals and classes; for many years, groups and teams have been used to promote competition, particularly in the secondary school. However, some teachers have recognised the value of using groups to encourage cooperative learning in support of personal growth. The utopia of a classroom healthy with the mutual respect of its thriving membership is for many teachers a distant goal; yet it is increasingly recognised that this is the direction in which we should be heading. Developing and applying the teaching skills to get there is the major requirement.

Although close proximity is one important feature of group work, the mere fact that pupils are clustered together does not in itself ensure that positive learning outcomes occur. A number of features of group work require attention if the teacher is to maximise the potential richness of this organisational arrangement.

In this chapter, we consider groups *within the classroom* and examine some of the issues raised when working with a class of 20–30 young people. Rather than providing a checklist of 'do's' and 'don'ts' we will focus on four main areas of this less-didactic form of teaching and student-centred learning:

1 From whole class to small groups
2 The learning environment:
   - group size
   - group composition
   - physical arrangements
   - the task
3 The role of the teacher
   - establishing work relationships
   - monitoring and supporting
   - ending the task
4 The rights and responsibilities of pupils

1 From whole class to small groups

In Figure 2.a the pupils are seated in rows and face the teacher at the front of the classroom. This 'traditional' classroom arrangement has an orthodoxy based equally on furniture layout and teaching style. The single desks, or pairs, so often found in classrooms, create the pupils' personal territory. The control-based didactic process – with teacher as expert, mediating pupils' learning through the question and answer process – combines with the furniture to shut out positive pupil-pupil interactions. The fervour with which copying is outlawed and 'not quite perfect' verbal responses to open questions rejected on the strength of the one right answer in the teacher's mind, further works against attempts to demonstrate learners' capacity to work together in support of the individual's development.

In such a classroom set-up there is a temptation for the teacher to engage in discussion with certain members and claim that a 'class discussion' is in progress. The questions tend to be initiated by the teacher and responses may be invited from volunteers or identified individuals. At its worst this forces pupils into roles maintained by the normative controls of the peer group and the expectations of the teacher, setting those who are successful in teacher terms at odds with those who fail.

The 'traditional' classroom often has very clear territorial divides. The teacher's space is bounded by blackboard, table, chair and brief-case; the pupils' by desks arranged to face the teacher at the front. The teacher attempts to control all interactions by personal intervention. He establishes his territory in the classroom and pupils occupy their space; there may be occasions when the teacher 'invades' the pupils' territory, but seldom vice versa, except when work is to be marked.

In a configuration like that shown in Figure 2.a the majority of pupils are looking at the back of the pupil in front, so discussion is difficult. If desks are arranged in straight rows pupils can only readily communicate with the person sitting to their left and/or right. One of the prerequisites for effective communication in groups is that partici-pants can see each other's body language and, in particular, their facial expressions. In an attempt to engage the whole class in discussion the teacher may therefore adopt a circular or rectangular seating arrange-ment, with the pupils facing inwards to form a single group (see Figures 2.b and 2.c).

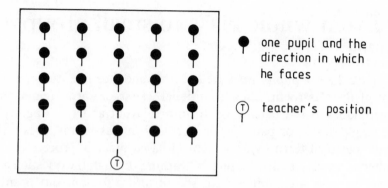

Fig. 2.a A class arranged in straight rows

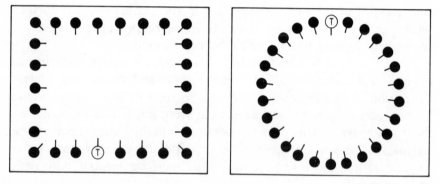

Fig. 2.b A rectangular seating arrangement   Fig. 2.c A circular setting arrangement

When this organisational pattern is first tried it is useful to ask the pupils to say how it differs from their previous experience, especially if the teacher is also seated in the ring. This task of telling each other can form the initial experience leading to more purposeful pupil-pupil interaction. However, as Figure 2.b indicates although people are facing towards the centre of the room, those seated along any one side may have difficulty in conducting a discussion with others sitting beyond their immediate neighbour. The numbers participating and the large amount of empty space in the centre may also inhibit pupils from sharing their views.

From our own experience in adult groups we are aware of the tensions and anxieties that prevent personal participation. We may judge our questions and answers to be too inconsequential or our ability to articulate clearly inadequate. Yet in the privacy of our car on the journey home or in the bath later that night our oratory flows! It is as if we need access to more private rehearsals for our thoughts before we are prepared to risk them in the wider group. The teacher who knows this to be true of himself will surely wish to facilitate the growth of his pupils' capacity to represent themselves well in public. This will require the organisation of sub-groups and, in turn, the application of other skills, as Kerry and Sands (1982) point out:

> The skill of teaching by using groups is an advanced teaching skill. To do it effectively the practitioner needs to possess already several basic skills such as the ability to teach the whole class together, to control them, to manage resources and to deal with individuals.

Even the effective class teacher may need to develop new competences for working with small groups, which in turn will affect that teacher's perception of his role in the learning situation (see sub-section 3 below).

2 The learning environment

Group size

In a situation where two people are engaged in discussion, there is likely to be a high level of personal participation; as the size of the group increases, the opportunity for individual contributions diminishes. It is difficult to be precise about an optimum group size, but we suggest that effective whole group interaction decreases as group size increases. However, as groups become more skilled at listening to the contributions of individuals, greater numbers can be accommodated.

Some teachers have responded to this suggestion by stating that it is not possible to create small groups within a large class. There may be real problems associated with, for example, lack of pupil and/or teacher experience, an unhelpful classroom layout, fixed furniture, poor pupil-teacher or pupil-pupil relationships and fear of collegial or parental disapproval. Nevertheless, we have found that an increasing number of teachers and pupils are gaining great satisfaction from small group work within their overall learning experience.

Where sub-groups contain more than eight members, it is helpful to negotiate a division of labour, whereby pairs and threes work on specific facets of the task before the group reconvenes to share its experience. Flexibility and mobility are key features of effective group work but this needs careful management. The movement of one pair or small group to join with another needs to be planned, so that groups in the same area of the room come together. With an inexperienced teacher or group the request to 'find another pair to work with' may lead to a breakdown of discipline. In the initial stages of developing such an approach the teacher must be vigorous and mobile, moving around the class to ensure, first of all, that the logistics of the operation are practicable and that sub-groups know exactly what is expected of them at the next stage.

Group composition

It is important to consider whether or not a group selected by the teacher is likely to work more effectively than one composed of pupils who have chosen to work together. In the latter case, there is a danger that the friendship base of self-selected groups will exclude isolates and 'enemies'. It may be that the teacher has to allocate such pupils to groups and thus the notion of self-selection is undermined. Friendship groupings may bring together 'birds of a feather', in that, for example, disruptive, self-assertive or withdrawn pupils may appear as separate groups. The strength of using friendship groupings is that existing good relationships ensure group cohesion. Equally this may lead to lower levels of debate, through members conforming to an established group view.

In a mixed class, the teacher may favour a situation where each group is composed of boys and girls, but if pupils are allowed to select they may not share this viewpoint. Similarly, pupils of similar ability and age may prefer to work together.

There is no absolute rule about the best way to organise groups, but with knowledge of the class the teacher is likely to know which selection process to adopt in order to provide meaningful learning experiences for the pupils.

If one of the aims of group work is to encourage pupils who do not normally work together to do so, then the teacher may determine the composition by selection or by a procedure that ensures random groupings. Although it is highly desirable to keep the peace it must be recognised that such 'cosy' arrangements are not going to be fully developmental. In life we all face moments of conflict; learning to deal creatively with turbulence is a skill we should aim to foster. In initially acceding to friendship groups the teacher should be aware of the limitations this brings and plan for the day when circumstances permit reorganisation. With experience and close knowledge of a group the teacher can develop effective 'antennae' to detect the opportunities for such reorganisation, and quick reactions to bring about change. Ideally this reactive mode leads to a proactive mode, when, through consultation with the participants, new organisational patterns anticipate new tasks.

No matter what stage of development a group has reached, the teacher must remember his responsibility for taking direct action and fostering this in others. If disagreement about group composition enervates the participants to such an extent that they cannot generate their own solution, it is clearly unproductive for the teacher to remain passive.

Physical arrangements

It is possible to involve pairs in discussion without a major change in the classroom layout, simply by asking each person to turn to face his partner (Figure 2.d). At this most simple level it is possible to enrich discussion by merely replacing the traditional prompts – 'Who can tell me . . . ?', 'What is the . . . ?', 'When did . . . ?' by the stem phrase 'Find out from your partner what they know about . . .'. When using this strategy the teacher needs to be fully mobile, listening in to the conversations he has initiated, and being particularly sensitive to those whose timidity prevents their public contribution.

Desks and tables may be placed between each pair to provide a shared work surface and engender a feeling of security; face-to-face interaction without any physical barrier may initially inhibit communication. However, if work surfaces are not required, desks and tables may be placed away from pairs or small groups.

In Figure 2.e, furniture is placed against the perimeter walls and the area in the middle of the room is devoted to group work. The advantage of this arrangement is that the teacher has close control over the situation and groups can easily be linked together. However if the area is small, the privacy of group work may be infringed and one group's discussion may interfere with that of another.

In Figure 2.f, the furniture is congregated in the central area. This enables each group to establish an area where its neighbour does not

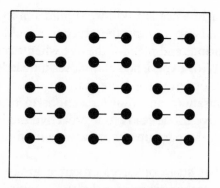

Fig. 2.d Paired work developed from rows

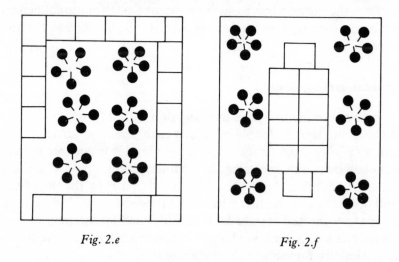

Fig. 2.e   *Fig. 2.f*

unduly interfere with its work. Such segregation may be ideal in situations where members find it difficult to focus on their group tasks.

Even in a room where there is fixed furniture – for example, a science laboratory – it is possible to have group discussion. Small groups clustered at the ends and middle of long benches (Figure 2.g) may join together to form larger groupings (Figure 2.h).

Whatever the setting, it is important that group members sit on seats of a similar height. Where people are seated at different levels, communication may be severely impeded.

As a general rule it is better to work in an area that is too large rather than too small, as groups may then be clearly identified as separate and movement problems can be reduced. Boundary markers, such as

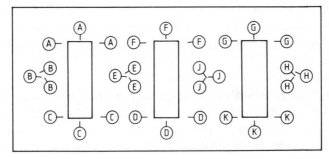

Fig. 2.g Working in threes

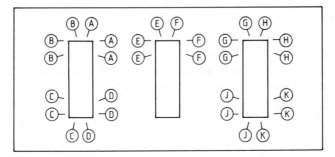

Fig. 2.h Linkage of groups of three

chairs, desks and tables, can be used to define the effective work space.

The teacher should produce a 'movement' chart which outlines the way in which groups are to be formed, amalgamated and reformed, particularly in the early stages of work with pupils.

The task

Generally, the task should be achievable and perceived as worthwhile by both learners and teacher. There may be occasions when a seemingly impossible task is set in order to make points relating to the need for corporate rather than individual action. There is, however, no virtue in pupils experiencing continual failure which may lead to negative attitudes and behaviour.

The essential guideline is to start from where the pupils are; from the position of their existing skills, knowledge and experience. To fail in this is to devalue the understanding pupils already have (and the process whereby they acquired it) and to cast adrift those who cannot bridge the gap between past experience and current expectations.

There are a number of strategies for establishing where learners are in their present experience. The two set out below may be used in connection with many of the activities described in this book.

The round

With the class functioning as one group, individuals are asked to make a comment about themselves in the context of an agreed task. For example, group members embarking on a new project, say diet, may be asked to complete the statement 'When I think about the word diet I . . . ' or 'To me diet means . . . '

When using this approach it is important to give the group members a brief period, perhaps 30 seconds, to think about their answers before starting the round. Always invite someone to start the process and go round in one direction. Remember the 'pass' rule. Everyone has the right to pass rather than make a statement and during the round comments on individual contributions are to be avoided.

Answers I already know

For this approach each pupil will need a piece of paper and a pencil. Everyone is invited to think of a question related to the topic – to which they already know the answer. The question is written out on the piece of paper and folded up. When everyone is ready the class moves around rapidly exchanging bits of paper. The task then is to find out the answers to the questions from whichever member of the group knows them. By displaying all the questions and answers the group gets a view of its own resources, and this forms the starting point for subsequent work.

In a class where there is a wide range of needs and interests, the provision of a challenging task for all pupils on all occasions may be difficult to accomplish. The teacher who seeks to offer learning opportunities that require different personal and social skills over a period of time goes a great way towards accommodating individual abilities and aptitudes.

For any work session it is important to make sure that the necessary resources are readily available so that there is a smooth transition from one phase of activity to another. The distribution of resources within the room will also require careful planning in order to assist ease of access and reduce the need for queueing. With a particular activity or task in mind, the reader may wish to consider how he would distribute resources in the classrooms represented by Figures 2.e–2.h.

Using experience from outside the group

Leslie Button, in his books *Developmental Group Work with Adolescents* and *Group Tutoring for the Form Teacher* developed the interlinked concepts of learners going out from the school to carry out an enquiry and learners receiving and taking responsibility for visitors to their group. In the *Active Tutorial Work* materials (Lancashire County Council) these same ideas are fully developed and incorporated into programmes of work for tutorial time. The reader is directed to these books for background reading. The application of these ways of working should not be restricted to pastoral settings; they lend themselves to a full range of curriculum areas, and in particular to the type of work covered by this book.

We are all inquisitive; even those of us with low levels of 'the desire to know' find it hard to resist turning round when we hear the fire engine's bell, or picking up on our fellow travellers' conversations. Young children are exceptionally inquisitive and most of us mourn the loss of this instinct in many older pupils.

Engaging in the process of enquiry builds on the learner's need to know. The principles are quite straightforward. Within any aspect of learning or topic for study there is likely to be a number of questions to be resolved. The ten areas covered in this book offer many rich avenues for enquiry.

Carrying out an enquiry
Stage one in the process is to identify and agree the need for further information of a kind that can realistically be investigated within the immediate environment of the school or pupils' homes.

Stage two is to discuss in small groups exactly what it is that the group needs to know. This is usually set out as a number of questions.

Stage three is to share these questions between the sub-groups in order to come to a consensus view for all participants.

Stage four is to carry out the enquiry. With an inexperienced group it is helpful to role play the questioning process and give pupils practice in initiating conversations within the enquiry. This should be carried out in support groups and all members should be given time to prepare themselves for the task. Less confident pupils will need extra support; on the first few occasions it may be best if they work with more confident members. It is important to make clear that this is intended to prepare them for taking on the role of questioner.

Many teachers have expressed anxiety about young pupils carrying out enquiries outside of school. Dangerous roads, 'don't talk to strangers' and fears of the mischief children get up to all combine to weaken the teacher's confidence to give it a go. Of course, we do not advocate putting the pupils at risk – the teachers themselves should play a full part in the enquiry alongside the pupils. One solution to these initial fears is to organise the class into support groups which work closely together. These should not exceed four members; a larger group size will intimidate some people when questioned. Larger groups also reduce the scope for active participation. The groups can then be accompanied to a 'safe' place, perhaps a shopping precinct, an old people's home or a community centre, and allowed to work within this environment.

Alternatively, the enquiry can be carried out among the family and neighbours of each pupil and this alternative should not be undervalued.

Stage five requires the pupils to report back the results of their enquiry, to share this information and to act on it. The action may be to formulate another enquiry, or it could be to plan a different activity. Ideally the products of the enquiry inform the pupil's position in a decision making mode, and the options that exist become clearer.

Receiving a visitor
One option is to seek advice or further information from an 'expert'. A particularly effective way of using experts is to receive them as visitors to the group. The traditional view of a visitor to a class is someone who comes to speak to the group about their particular subject area. The emphasis is on what the expert knows; it is generally assumed that the expert also knows what the pupils want to know or that the pupils don't know what they want to know. This mode of operation is often ineffective, it requires the pupils to be politely passive while listening, yet quick and perceptive with their questions at the end. How many embarrassed teachers have sweated through the pupils' silent lack of response to the speaker's invitation 'Are there any questions?'

The very word 'receiving' in the phrase 'receiving a visitor' should set the context of the event. The onus is on the pupils to deal with the visitor, both in a social sense and in terms of the information required. With inexperienced groups it is crucial that their first experience of this very useful way of working is with a sensitive and understanding visitor who is well briefed and prepared to let the group take the lead.

As adults we tend not to deal with young peoples' silences very well. We fill them with our own comments, thereby preventing the pupil who is on the very edge of an intervention from coming forwards. Of course, a prolonged silence not only embarrasses everyone but erodes the group's self-confidence. A sensitive balance needs to be struck between the initiative coming from the group and careful prompting by the visitor. Receiving visitors is always a source of social experience and offers many opportunities for development. A number of specific roles for group members can be assigned: collecting the visitor and bringing her to the group, introducing her to the group, initiating the questioning process, bringing the session to a close and accompanying the visitor to her car, the bus stop or some other part of the school.

The key to success in this process is sound preparation of the group, both in terms of the specific roles individuals will take and the questions that will be used to stimulate conversation. Regarding timing, 20 minutes is usually the maximum period initially. As groups become experienced at receiving visitors and incorporating the outcomes of their own enquiries into the conversation the time-span can be increased. We have experience of extremely effective work with visitors going on for an hour or even longer.

Who are these visitors and where do they come from? Schools are surrounded by potential visitors; other members of staff; members of the non-teaching staff; teachers from other schools; parents; education office staff; school advisers; governors; employees in local government departments, hospitals, clinics or local industry; members of trade unions or voluntary bodies. The list is endless.

Though the two approaches have been described separately they in effect form an interlocking pair of strategies to form a cyclical process of enquiry.

3 The role of the teacher

Establishing a working relationship

At the outset, pupils and teachers need to negotiate a 'contract' whereby they establish the ground rules of their working relationship. The creation of a trusting environment is a basic requirement for work which emphasises the importance of sharing and valuing other people's views. This aspect of teaching/learning is present in all classroom situations. The only difference here is the suggestion that the pupils have a positive part to play in the process of establishing the ground rules. As suggested earlier, this does raise the issue of class control and responsibility. Giving pupils the opportunity to contribute their own ideas does not take away authority or control from the teacher. Instead, it not only gives the teacher support from the group but also fosters pupil self-control, the quality so highly prized by all who would judge the outcomes of the education process.

One very effective way of establishing good working relationships in a group is through 'brainstorming'. The advantage of this technique is that it rapidly generates ideas without the restriction of attributing particular value to individual suggestions. With an inexperienced class it may be helpful to work in small groups. It may also be helpful if a 'dummy run' is carried out to establish the way of working. Both these factors are assumed in the following model:

1 Divide the class into small groups.
2 Choose an object with which all participants will be familiar – a glass bottle, the school minibus, a tennis racket . . .
3 Invite each group to choose a 'scribe' and issue this person with a thick felt-tip pen and a large piece of paper.
4 Ask the groups to suggest as many uses as possible for the chosen object. The scribe lists all the contributions as quickly as possible, with no discussion, and no reactions to suggestions. (A maximum of 3 minutes is given to this stage.)
5 Collect feedback from the groups (one suggestion at a time per group). Write the suggestions up on large sheets of paper, again without commenting or attributing value.

Up to this point the process merely generates ideas. After this, (when the model is applied to 'real' situations), the group is asked to identify those suggestions considered by the majority to be practical and workable.

6 A vote is taken on individual suggestions, each person being allowed to vote for a maximum of 3 suggestions.
7 The list of items voted for becomes the basis of the group's related task, until circumstances dictate that change is necessary, at which time the process is repeated.

(With an experienced group stages 1 and 2 can be omitted.)

In order to establish ground rules for some of the activities in this book, the teacher might ask: 'What do we need to do in order to work well in a group?', and then follow the process described above.

An alternative approach for inexperienced pupils might be for groups to display their response sheets in the classroom for other pupils to read. Points of convergence and divergence can then be identified and any group member can return to his group's sheet to add a further item – although at this stage nobody has the right to delete any contribution. After a period of observation, the group returns to its original site to construct a set of ground rules which contain the common elements of the displays. The teacher asks one group to offer its ground rules and records these on a large sheet of paper. The other groups are invited to offer items not previously included.

The teacher checks with the whole class that there is consensus support for the recorded items (see Figure 2.i) and the negotiated contract remains on display for subsequent lessons. The class may wish to review the contract from time to time.

No shouting out
Listen
Give everyone a chance to talk
Be honest
Trust each other
Be kind
Don't swear
Show you're interested
Someone take notes (not me!)
Look after the room
Be nice to each other
Look after the furniture

Fig. 2.i   Example of negotiated contract

Through this process, the teacher provides the pupils with an opportunity to establish the group's own code of practice. The 'contract' is expressed in pupil terms. The teacher does not become redundant in this situation but uses his skills to monitor and support pupil activity.

Monitoring and supporting

Inevitably, there are times when the teacher engages simultaneously in both monitoring and supporting. In order to carry out these tasks effectively the teacher needs to be aware of all that is going on in the room. For example, the teacher may have good peripheral vision if he faces towards the centre of the room (Figure 2.j) whereas his ability to monitor is reduced if he attends to one group and faces towards a corner or a wall (Figure 2.k).

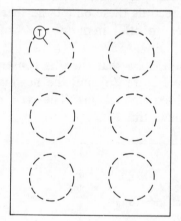

Fig. 2.j Good peripheral vision   *Fig. 2.k Poor peripheral vision*

Most important of all is the teacher's mobility about the room. Rather than being a member of a particular group, he needs to be free to work alongside individuals and groups as the occasion arises.

Clearly the teacher's involvement with any one group reduces his ability to monitor class activity, irrespective of his position within the room. He may more effectively monitor class activity from a standing position where – by virtue of his height above the seated participants – he can exercise greater influence over proceedings. Even where verbal exchanges are inaudible, the teacher may be able to detect from the body language of group members how the task is being approached. By standing near a group, the teacher may clearly signal his interest, even if he is watching what other groups are doing. If the teacher joins a group, he should crouch or sit so that his head height corresponds with that of other group members.

Groups respond differently to the close proximity of the teacher. Some become dependent upon his contribution, others are intimidated and discussion is stifled. The teacher's presence is likely to influence the dynamics of the group and individual pupils will react differently. The shy pupil may gain support from the teacher's unobtrusive closeness; the teacher may help such a pupil to formulate ideas and may encourage a verbal contribution.

With pupils who find it difficult to contribute to whole group discussion the teacher will need to be very sensitive to signs of their readiness to participate. Shifting on a chair, an intake of breath, or rapid eye movements may all signal the intention to speak. The teacher may need to hold back the more vocal group members and encourage the shy person. Crouching beside the pupil, the teacher may invite a one-to-one comment and judge if the person will repeat it to one or two others in the sub-group. After further encouragement and rehearsal, the time may be reached when the individual will comment briefly to the whole class, with the teacher standing by. With more time and some success, the pupil will be able to talk to the group with the teacher standing at a distance. Over a sequence of such occasions the teacher will begin to withdraw eye contact with the speaker to deflect their words to others in the class; thus the timid person will grow in self confidence and gradually free himself from his fear of contributing.

A pupil who dominates the group may intimidate those who are less confident and this situation may provide an early opportunity for the teacher to invite groups to reflect upon 'the contract'. For both the shy and the over-zealous pupil, the teacher may discuss their participation in a private one-to-one exchange.

Ending the task

When the teacher wishes to ask the whole class to stop work he should bear in mind that it is difficult for a group to pick up its discussion after an interruption. If the teacher stops an individual group to clarify the task, check on progress or negotiate new directions and developments, he can allow other groups at their various stages to continue to operate. However, if the teacher judges that it would be in the pupils' interest to share aspects of common concern across the class, then the full attention of all pupils should be sought. It is best to forewarn groups that this is going to happen by stating a timescale. Where pupils are working in small groups (see Figure 2.l), it may be necessary to form one large circle to ensure that pupil attention is gained for a plenary or report-back session (Figure 2.m).

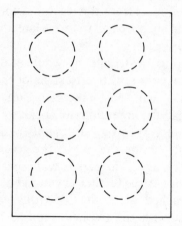

Fig. 2.l Small groups working in circles

Fig. 2.m Large circle formed from small circles

Where an overhead projector, blackboard or wall display is to be used the small groups will need to open out into horseshoe formation so that no pupil has his back to the recording area (Figure 2.n).

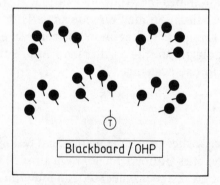

Fig. 2.n Horseshoe formation

It is important that pupils' work is always acknowledged and valued even if the outcomes are not as anticipated by the teacher. A negative comment, casual aside or unsympathetic glance can do much to undermine the self-esteem and self-confidence of an individual or a group.

If there is to be a public report-back session, the teacher should ask the individual or the group if a particular comment or issue may be shared. In the early stages the pupils may be reluctant to communicate their views, and will require the prompts and support of the teacher. However, it is the views of pupils that are important rather than the teacher's interpretation of their views.

The preparation of an agreed statement by a group will help to ensure that diverse as well as similar views are represented. The teacher works for the occasion when groups nominate their own spokesperson, but initially it may be necessary for the teacher to take direct action by requesting a group member to take on the role.

Report-back sessions may serve a number of purposes, for example, to reinforce positive learning, share common tasks or provide possible growth points for future work. It is not necessary, or even desirable, to end every lesson with a report from groups; plenary sessions can become a boring experience if each group conveys the same message.

Role play in group work

Offering learners the opportunity to try out new ways of behaving or responding, through working in role, is a powerful strategy. Much has been written about this and the reader is directed to the work of Bolton (1980) and O'Neill *et al* (1977). The value of role play lies in the post-play or debriefing, where pupils are invited to reflect upon the experience of being someone else or viewing a situation from a new personal perspective.

If role play is used, it is important that pupils 'de-role' at the conclusion of the activity, so that they take on their own persona. This can be achieved by setting tasks which require the pupils to come out of role, for example, asking them to reflect on their experiences when in a role different from their usual self. It is important that all the participants fully understand that they have re-established their usual identity.

Whatever the final activity of the session, it is important that it is planned as carefully as the main body of the lesson.

4 The rights and responsibilities of pupils

Apart from respect for and adherence to the negotiated contract, a major learning theme for pupils is the acceptance of the notion of 'the normality of difference' – ie it is normal for each person to perceive the world differently and thus to hold different attitudes, beliefs and values. If this notion is accepted, it is inconceivable that people will respond to every situation similarly. An effective way of illustrating this point is by displaying the shape below (Figure 2.o) to a group and inviting each member to consider privately what it represents.

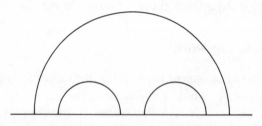

Fig. 2.o What is this figure?

Then the participants are asked to reveal what the figure means to them. Pupils have suggested some of the following:

A straight line, large semi-circle and two arcs
A semi-detached igloo
The rear view of someone kneeling on the floor
A fat person lying on the beach
A fat person standing on the edge of a diving board
A bald-headed man looking over a wall
Twin tunnels

It takes time for pupils to accept each other's similarities and differences; therefore consistency of sub group membership is to be encouraged when the whole group is being established. It is relatively easy to be dismissive of those people who are considered to be 'different' but hard to work with them on cooperative and collaborative ventures. Certainly in a multi-ethnic classroom, tolerance and understanding of people who have different experiences of life presents a formidable challenge for young people.

Every created group should provide support for its members which the teacher facilitates through the provision of appropriate learning opportunities. It is hoped that the experiences gained in the classroom will lead to caring relationships being established beyond the confines of the school. Pupils should be encouraged to use their abilities and aptitudes to enhance their own personal growth and to contribute to the well-being of others. No pupil should feel 'disadvantaged' ie that his/her contribution is inadequate, inferior, inappropriate or irrelevant.

This philosophy underpins all the activities in this book. Our aim is to demonstrate to all participants in the learning process that working with groups has many advantages both in school and in a wide range of social settings throughout life.

References
Bolton, G. *Towards a therapy of drama in education* Harlow: Longman, 1980
Button, L. *Developmental Group Work with Adolescents* Hodder and Stoughton, 1976
Button, L. *Group tutoring for the form teacher*, (Books 1 & 2) London: Hodder and Stoughton, 1982
Kerry, T. and Sands, M. *Handling classroom groups*, (DES Teacher Education Project) London: Macmillan Education, 1982
Lancashire County Council *Active tutorial work*, (Books 1–6) Oxford: Basil Blackwell, 1978–83
O'Neill, C., Lambert, A., Linnell, R. and Warr–Wood, J. *Drama guidelines* London: Heinemann, 1977

The Activities

Introduction

The following chapters are written in a consistent format. They each have a general introduction intended to set the scene for the whole chapter, followed by a number of activities. Each activity also has a brief introduction followed by a statement of objectives, a list of materials required, explanation of the procedure to be adopted and a number of suggestions for follow-up work.

We hope that the activities will be fun and provide enjoyment as well as opportunities for team-work and the development of support in groups. In designing the activities we have borne in mind the need to keep costs to a minimum. A4 paper, newsprint, off-cuts of card, felt-tip pens and pencils form the main resource requirements for most activities. We consider that the *major* resource is the pupil.

It is crucially important to state clear objectives for the work to be undertaken. It is not enough for a teacher to say 'I haven't articulated my objectives, but if you come to the lesson you will see what I am trying to do.' Such an approach fails to provide reliable indicators of the teacher's and learner's intentions or a sound basis for judging the extent to which they have been realised.

Grouping

Many of the activities in the next ten chapters require pupils to work in groups of different kinds. Below are examples of some of the ways in which these can be formed.

1 Forming random pairs
Write out sufficient sets of character cards for everyone in the class to have one from a pair. Pin the cards on the pupils' backs, at random, and invite each person to find their partner. You could vary the activity by allowing pupils to ask questions on one occasion, or by suggesting the use of mime on another. Examples of character pairs could be Morecambe and Wise, Laurel and Hardy, Donald Duck and Mickey Mouse.

2 Random groupings

Produce a set of birth sign cards (check the class register to see that the pattern of distribution is fairly even). Arrange the signs around the room. Invite the pupils to go and stand by their sign, and form the clusters of pupils into groups.

3 Pre-set group numbers

Use sets of playing cards to arrange the required number of groupings and members in each group. Hand out sets of each suit – clubs, spades, diamonds and hearts. If more than four groups are needed you could use the face cards – Jacks, Queens and Kings.

Alternatively, use pieces of coloured card. Decide on the number of groups needed, use the same number of colours and cut out enough squares of each to fit the pattern required. Hand out the pieces at random and invite the pupils to find their partners.

'Family' cards can be used in a similar way. Produce a set of cards for fruits, animals or plants using the number of family members required for the group composition, eg father grape, mother grape, young grape and baby grape. Hand the cards out at random and invite the groups to find their family members.

The last three activities can be made competitive, if this is felt to be appropriate, by challenging the last group to form to do a forfeit.

4 Friendship groups

These lend themselves both to random-sized groups or pairs. Such groups form an ideal basis for work requiring considerable support. However, in choosing friendship as a basis for group formation ensure that this will not isolate individuals or compound existing isolation for those outside established friendship groups.

3 Who am I?

The question '*Who am I?*' may seem absurd, as the answer appears to be obvious – for example, '*I am me*' or '*I am Rudi*'. However, such responses offer no information beyond a label of personal identification. To dismiss a seemingly simple question may be to undervalue its significance.

Unlike many inanimate objects, a person is not likely to be perceived similarly by everyone; he will be viewed and valued differently by each person. He will gain an impression of who he is and of his personal worth not just from within himself, but from the way in which others behave towards him. Therefore the context and setting in which he interacts with others will have a profound effect upon his self-concept and self-esteem.

In common parlance, the term 'being two-faced' is usually derogatory, but in reality it may be a more positive expression of the human condition, implying that one is seen as being 'multi-faceted', even though one has a high level of personal integrity! The expectations of others demand that each of us plays particular roles in a particular way given particular contexts or settings. For example, a father who hugs his teenage daughter in celebration of a sporting achievement may, when playing the role of teacher, find that a similar behaviour with a pupil is totally unacceptable.

Thus, 'who I am' is not a fixed state, but a condition in which we respond to circumstances. Social norms do influence an individual's behaviour to some extent, but there remains an opportunity for the idiosyncracies which mark 'me' out from 'you' to be expressed.

The romantic notion of love at first sight may be true in some cases, but we cannot assume that positive first impressions always prove to be well-founded over a period of time. Similarly, to reject someone on the basis of one encounter or on the opinion of a third party, may be unreasonable. For better or worse, time may cause us to comment: 'You are not who I thought you were,' or 'A little knowledge can be dangerous'!

The activities in this chapter are designed to stimulate discussion about the personal identity of oneself and others.

The first activity, *Find someone who . . .* focuses upon a way of encouraging pupils to gain insights into the world of other people in the class. The level of self-disclosure is set through an agenda devised by the teacher. The activity is particularly useful as an 'ice-breaker' with a class which has recently been formed. Although pupils will get to know each other in time, this exercise has the potential to accelerate the 'getting to know you' process.

What's in a name? invites pupils to look at the importance of their name beyond that of being a label. The use of forenames and/or surnames in particular settings may indicate the nature of the authority relationships and social conventions.

There may be a tendency for young people to believe that they make friendships with people who are like themselves. While in general terms this may be true, there are likely to be features in their lives that are dissimilar to those of their friends. Also, it may be the case that people who see themselves as sharing very few common attitudes, beliefs and values, may on further investigation find convergent experiences in their lives. The notion of the 'normality of difference' is explored in the section *Same but different.*

In *Sunshine faces* pupils record some of the differences between their first or primary school and their middle or secondary school experience. For each identified difference, they are asked to recall their feelings on the first day in the new school and to note how their views have changed over time. The activity highlights how a shared experience can be perceived differently from individual to individual. The implications of seeing the world differently are considerable and may indicate why people often find it difficult to reach a consensus.

Given this phenomenon, *Small ads* encourages pupils to identify the attributes and characteristics which they value in others. Through the process of writing about a fictitious person, the pupil may become involved in self-examination, finding out what he likes and dislikes about himself in the process.

If the uniqueness of the person has been emphasised, the section *Sometimes I worry about* . . . will redress the balance so that pupils examine common anxieties and concerns.

For pupils who have a poor opinion of themselves, the activity *The magic box tells me* may help to improve their self-esteem. It may come as a surprise that they can be considered as VIPs. As trust builds up with the class, the activity, *I am* . . . may be helpful to pupils in showing how their view of themselves compares with that of a friend.

The final activity, *Another brick in the wall* provides an opportunity for class members to make positive comments about each other. It is important that one receives such 'positive strokes' in order to reiterate and reinforce a feeling of individual and collective well-being among young people.

3.1 Find someone who . . .

This activity offers an opportunity for pupils coming together for the first time to get to know more about each other and to break down inhibitions about working with 'strangers'. Although familiarity and friendships will occur naturally, you may wish to encourage the development of a cooperative learning environment as quickly as possible.

You need to have sufficient knowledge about class members so that the items included on the *Find someone who* . . . sheet are applicable to *at least* two pupils. The list should be designed so that no pupil feels embarrassed or distressed by the inclusion of a particular item.

The activity involves movement so a clear space should be made available, perhaps by placing furniture around the walls. The activity may also generate quite a lot of noise, as pupils engage in conversation.

Before the session, prepare numbered cards so that random groups of four may be created, ie for a class of 28 pupils there will be sets of four cards, each numbered 1–7 inclusive.

Later in the life of the class the activity could be used with different items. Invite pupils to offer three or four items, then select the more unusual ones as a challenge to, and extension of, pupils' knowledge of each other.

Objectives

- to show that people build up a picture of who they are from meeting and working with other people
- to provide an opportunity for pupils to learn more about each other

Materials

A copy of the *Find someone who* . . . sheet for each pupil
Pencils

Procedure

a Issue each pupil with a proforma and a pencil. Explain that a pupil may ask another pupil about any two items on the list. For example:
  Sam asks Jo:
    'Do you keep a diary?' Jo says 'No'.
    'Do you like tennis?' Jo says 'Yes'.
  On his own sheet, Sam writes Jo's name against item 9. Jo may wish to ask Sam about two items, for example:
    'Do you like tennis?' Sam says 'Yes'.
    'Do you have a dog?' Sam says 'Yes'.
  On her sheet, Jo writes Sam's name against items 9 and 7. They move off to continue this process with other pupils. The pupil who completes his proforma first is asked to inform the teacher.

b You may need to work alongside a pupil who feels shy or is experiencing difficulty with the process. It will be helpful to further activity if pupils record five or six names.

c When the first pupil signals the completion of his form, tell the class to stop work. Read out the name against each item to check that it has been correctly recorded. If the names are correct, you could continue the activity for a further period of time *or* use the first pupil's response as a means of terminating the activity.

d Hand out the numbered cards and ask a pupil to shuffle them. He gives approximately half of the cards to another pupil. The cards are 'dealt' face downwards to all members of the class. Invite pupils to walk around and find people who have the same number. When the groups have been formed, they locate themselves throughout the room.

e Using their activity sheets as a basis for discussion, group members identify the items which they have in common and compile additional shared experiences and skills on the reverse side of *one* sheet. (10–15 minutes)

f Invite each group in turn to share an item which they think may not be contained on anyone else's list. This procedure may be continued for one or more cycles.

Prompts for reflection

● I was surprised that other people felt . . .
● I was pleased to know that . . .
● This session has helped me to . . .

Suggestions for follow-up work

Ask members of each random group to discuss what experiences, features or skills they share. From these characteristics, members design a logo which conveys the uniqueness of their group. Each group's contribution is displayed and an explanation of its meaning is conveyed to the class.

The activity may be extended so that a motto is added.

Find someone who . . .

Name

1 collects records   ....

2 dislikes ice-cream   ....

3 plays the piano   ....

4 keeps a diary   ....

5 walks to school   ....

6 was born more
   than twenty miles
   from school   ....

7 has a dog   ....

8 has an older sister   ....

9 likes tennis   ....

10 watches television
   every evening   ....

3.2 What's in a name?

A person's name is not only a label, it may have great significance for that individual and for members of his family. Prospective parents often spend many hours pondering upon suitable names for their pending offspring; considering and rejecting many before they find the most acceptable one. The name(s) finally selected may reflect identification with a famous or respected person within or outside the family, be associated with someone who featured in an earlier life experience, or have been in the family for successive generations. Of course, not all names are selected by these criteria – they may be suggested by other people, come from published lists of names or, on occasion, arise from an intuitive response immediately prior to the baby's arrival or registration.

A pupil who has been adopted or fostered, or who has lost close relatives, may perhaps be upset by situations where he is required to reveal the source of his name. Also, a pupil with an 'unusual' name may become the subject of ridicule unless the class has worked together over a period of time.

This activity may be used to lead on to consideration of name-calling and other forms of bullying. This, in turn may pave the way for pupils and teachers to feel confident enough to discuss more sensitive issues related to labelling and stereotyping. Space F on the *What's in a name* activity sheet (page 52) has been left empty so that you can write in a question which you feel is of particular importance or interest to the group.

Objectives

- to examine the importance of first names or names of referral in one's life

Materials

Plain A4 paper
Copies of the *What's in a name?* question sheet (p. 52) for each pair
Pencils

Procedure

a Give each pupil a plain sheet of A4 paper. Explain that pupils should write their names vertically down the left-hand side (see Figure 3.a).

a	b
J	Jokey
O	Open
H	Honest
N	Nice
P	Pleasing
E	Easy to get on with
A	Active
R	Reliable
C	Calm
E	Even-tempered

Fig. 3.a Example of a filled-out sheet

b In pairs, pupils help each other to write words or phrases against each of the letters in their names, which describe positive attributes or characteristics of the named person (see Figure 3.a). It may be difficult to think of a suitable response to some letters and easy to write more than one response to others; pupils should be made aware that this is acceptable, after they have spent some time trying to respond to each letter. (15 minutes)

c Following this warm-up exercise, give each pair a copy of the questions on page 52.

d Each pair selects (or is allocated) one question and writes their responses in note form on the other side of the sheet. Within a class, there may be two or three pairs working on the same question. It is important that *at least* two pairs work independently on a question, even if not all the questions are used. (5–10 minutes)

e The pairs who have been working on the same question come together to compare and contrast their responses. (5 minutes) Invite comments on the importance of the name by which one is called by friends; parents; teachers.

Prompts for reflection

- My name is important to me because . . .
- If someone uses my first name I feel . . .
- A world without first names would be . . .

Suggestions for follow-up work

1 Invite small groups to gather information through questionnaires or planned interviews (taped or video-recorded). Enquiries could include:

- a survey of the prevalence of certain names within particular age groups (for example 5–10-year-olds, 11–16s, 17–22s)
- choosing two or three first names and investigating why people were given them
- asking members of three or four families how they and their relatives came to be given their particular first names

Pupils themselves should compile the list of questions they wish to ask; this will provide them with an opportunity to determine just what they wish to investigate. The process of administration, analysis and reporting-back is for the pupils to determine, in consultation with the teacher.

2 Ask each pupil to trace his family tree.

3 Within the class there may be pupils who, for cultural reasons, are not referred to by their 'first' name. Pupils from a range of backgrounds could discuss and explain the conventions and customs of naming individuals within their own communities.

What's in a name?

A

If you were to have a son, what first name would you give him? Why?

B

If you were to have a daughter, what first name would you give her? Why?

C

How would you feel if people *never* referred to you by your first name?

D

How do you feel when people call you names?

E

What first name would you have chosen for yourself? Why?

F

3.3 Same but different

For this activity chairs and tables should be placed against the walls so as to provide a large area for unimpeded movement within the room. On one wall the letter **A** is displayed and on the opposite wall, the letter **B**.

The items listed in the central column of the proforma (page 56) are arbitrary; you should select ones which are appropriate for class members.

This activity is best used with pupils who know and respect each other and where all pupils may readily find a partner. So that pupils do not immediately focus upon similarities and differences in each other's private world, the activity encourages them to focus upon 'Things that you like and dislike about living in this area'. However, you may wish to place less rigid boundaries on the agenda, if you feel confident that pupils will be sensitive in discussing issues that have the potential to cause personal distress.

As well as its more obvious application, the activity may provide a suitable introduction for the consideration of cultural, gender, racial and religious similarities and differences among people within a local, regional, national and international context.

Objectives

- to show that even though friends may share many common features and interests in their lives, they may also have differences.

Materials

One *Same but different* sheet (p. 56) for each pupil
Pencils

Procedure

a Give each pupil a *Same but different* sheet and a pencil.
b Invite pupils to find a partner with whom they are friendly or who they know well. Each person writes the name of his partner at the bottom of the proforma.

c Explain how the activity operates, using Example 1 at the top of the sheet:

'This example is concerned with your liking for or dislike of cabbage. If you like cabbage, please stand by wall **A**; if you dislike cabbage, stand by wall **B**.'

Give pupils time to move to one of the two positions and continue:

'If your friend is standing by the same wall, put a circle around the word 'same' alongside the word 'cabbage' – you can see that this has already been done for the example. If your friend is standing by the opposite wall, put a circle around the word 'different'.'

d Pupils follow the same procedure for the other eight items at the top of the sheet as follows (Figure 3.b):

Item	Wall A	Wall B
Ice-cream	likes . . .	dislikes . . .
France	has been to . . .	has not been to . . .
Dog	has a . . .	does not have a . . .
London	has been to . . .	has not been to . . .
Eyes	has blue . . .	has non-blue . . .
Brother	has a . . .	does not have a . . .
Bicycle	has a . . .	does not have a . . .
Bus	travels to school by . . .	does not travel to school by . . .

Fig. 3.b

After each item, the pupil records whether he is standing by the 'same' wall as his partner or a 'different' one. (20 minutes)

e Ask pupils to sit down in their pairs.

'For ten minutes, discuss things that you like and dislike about living in this area. If you both like or dislike the same thing, write it down in the *same* column; if one of you likes and the other person dislikes the same thing, write it down in the *different* column.'

f Invite each pair to consider which parts of the information they shared they would be willing to tell another pair in the room. Each pair writes down on the back of a sheet what they learned about each other and were willing to share. (5–7 minutes)
g Ask pairs to form groups of four. Each pair is labelled A or B. Pair A talk for 3 or 4 minutes about their shared information while pair B listen. Then the situation is reversed.

Prompts for reflection

- I was surprised to learn that . . .
- I am like my friend (or partner) because . . .
- I realised during this lesson that . . .

Suggestions for follow-up work

1 In groups of four, ask pupils to talk about ways in which pupils of their age in another (identified) part of the country might be similar to or different from themselves.
2 As 1, but the social context is broadened to include other countries.

Same but different

Example 1

Same (circled)	Cabbage	Different
Same	Ice-cream	Different
Same	France	Different
Same	Dog	Different
Same	London	Different
Same	Eyes	Different
Same	Brother	Different
Same	Bicycle	Different
Same	Bus	Different

Same	**Different**

Name of friend ....

3.4 Sunshine faces

There are occasions when through reflection upon particular changes or transitions in our own lives we may be able to allay the fears of others who are about to undergo a similar experience. The example given is related to changing schools, particularly the transition from first or primary school to middle or secondary school.

Young people, just as much as adults, have the ability to assist in the personal and social development of others. Through this activity pupils are asked to examine their *feelings* at the time of entry into their present school and then to consider the feelings which they *now* have about the same issues. It is hoped that the comparison will encourage them to take action (perhaps as suggested) to help newcomers settle.

The *Sunshine faces* sheet (page 60) may be used in order to explore feelings about a set of ten other items, for example:

- colours
- foods
- school subjects
- sports
- roles, eg policeman, fireman, nurse
- television programmes

For pupils with reading difficulties the left-hand column may contain motifs, pictures or symbols.

Objectives

- to examine personal feelings about primary-secondary school transition
- to consider how our fears and aspirations change over time

Materials

One sheet of blank paper for each group of four.
One copy of the *Sunshine faces* sheet for each pupil
One blue/black and one red pen or crayon for each pupil.

Procedure

a Ask pupils to stand in line in order of *date* of birthday; pupils with birthdays on or near the first day of a month at the back of the line, and those born on the 30th or 31st of a month at the front. Starting at the back, pupils form groups of four according to this order, thus creating random groups.

b Each group of four finds a place to sit. Hand out sheets of blank paper and pens/crayons, and ask groups to nominate one member as 'scribe'. Invite groups to suggest ten differences between their primary school(s) and their present school, which the scribe records (see Figure 3.c).

More teachers
Movement from room to room
Bell rings
Bigger children
Bigger school
Travel to school by bus
New subjects
Homework
Uniform
New people

Fig. 3.c   Examples of differences between primary school and present school

c Give each pupil a copy of the *Sunshine Faces* sheet. Each pupil copies the ten items generated by his group in the left hand column.

d Ask each pupil to work privately and to use a *blue/black* pen or crayon. For each item, the pupil places a tick in the box under the 'face' which most accurately reflects his feelings *on the first day in this school.* (4–7 minutes)

e The pupil then uses a *red* pen or crayon to record his *present* feelings about the ten items.

f In fours, pupils discuss ways in which their feelings have changed over time.

g Invite each group to suggest ways in which its experience may be of benefit to next year's new pupils.

Prompts for reflection

- I found the change of school . . .
- I will always remember my first week in this school because . . .
- I will help new pupils to settle in this school by . . .

Suggestions for follow-up work

1 The class could design and write a school prospectus for next year's intake; this will involve the use of skills associated with, for example, research, collation, graphic design, editing and writing. Groups may negotiate a division of labour, to ensure that the available personal and collective talents are used for the mutual benefit of the class. (This project is likely to take weeks rather than days and demand a contractual commitment to ensure its completion.)
2 The class may wish to contribute to the induction programme for next year's intake, through the production of, for example

- a video about the school
- tutorial materials for use during the first few weeks
- individual letters to named pupils welcoming them to their new school

Sunshine faces

	Differences	1	2	3	4	5	6	7	8	9	10

3.5 Small ads

This activity leads pupils on from the identification of named individuals within the class or the school and encourages them to consider the attributes, characteristics and skills that they value in other people.

The 'small ad' format helps pupils use short sentences and phrases to provide clear and concise character profiles. For pupils who experience difficulties in expressing their views in writing, this process may offer a welcome alternative. However, you may need to help pupils whose handwriting or spelling can be difficult to decipher as contributions will be read by others.

Objectives

- to consider the qualities we value in other people
- to develop with peers a set of criteria for evaluating the 'ideal' person

Materials

One small card (or postcard) for each pupil
Pencils

Procedure

a Remind the class that local and national newspapers, journals and magazines carry small advertisements. Read out or display several 'small ads' to provide examples of the task that lies ahead.

b Give each pupil a piece of card and a pencil. Using no more than 20 words, each pupil uses the 'small ad' format to describe what he believes to be the 'ideal' person of his own age (for examples, see Figure 3.d). The writer decides upon a name for this fictitious character. (5–10 minutes)

Alan
Good at football. Willing to work hard at school. Helps his mother with washing up. Plays the trumpet.

Emma
Gets on well with her brothers and sisters. Visits her granny every Saturday. Digs the garden and plants vegetables.

Alex
Makes breakfast for his brothers. Looks after the cat, rabbits and hamsters. Helps with the shopping on Friday evenings.

Siobhan
Goes to church every Sunday. Cleans an old person's flat once a week. Washes the family car. Plays football.

Fig. 3.d.   Examples of the 'ideal' young person

c Collect all the cards.
d Divide the class into *an even number* of groups containing five or six. It is advisable for each group to gather around its own table or work surface.
e Give out the same number of cards as there are group members. Ask pupils to arrange the cards in rank order with the ideal person at the top of the table and so on down to the least ideal person at the bottom of the column. Explain that groups should agree on the order, since they will need to justify their decisions to another group shortly. (10–15 minutes)
f Pair up groups who are in close proximity; each group is labelled **A** or **B**. Group A explains the reasons for its rank order and group B is invited to ask questions. The groups then reverse roles.
g At the end of the activity, each group reconvenes to produce details of their ideal person (boy or girl).

Prompts for reflection

- There is no such person as an 'ideal person' because . . .
- It is important that all people should . . .
- I think I could help my parents by . . .
- I value people who are . . .
- One day, I hope to be . . .

Suggestions for follow-up work

1 Many schools now use various profiling procedures. An interesting follow-up activity might be to give pupils the opportunity to identify the criteria by which they wish to be appraised within the school setting.
2 Pupils could look for and collect obituaries in local newspapers and consider the range of attributes, contributions and skills that are valued in their community.

3.6 Sometimes I worry about . . .

The resource materials for this activity need to be prepared before the lesson takes place. Such sentence completion exercises appear throughout the book, and may be used to encourage pupils to generate their own materials. Pupils are more likely to take ownership of materials they have created than of those provided by adults. Here, the emphasis is on the development and utilisation of a pupil perspective.

Some time before the lesson, give each pupil a sheet containing three *Sometimes I worry about . . .* sentences (see page 67). Ask pupils to complete at least one of the sentences. This should be a private exercise, and pupils should not write their names on the paper. Collect in the papers, and on the basis of the pupils' responses identify six issues which are frequently mentioned as giving cause for concern, eg bullying, career prospects, examinations, homework, nuclear war, siblings . . .

Copy the sentences on to the *Sometimes I worry about . . .* pupil's sheet, in the spaces numbered 1–6. The advantage of the teacher recording the responses is that it prevents pupils being identified by their handwriting. This also gives you an opportunity to remove any sentence which is likely to cause offence. Photocopy the sheet and separate the responses so that each pupil in a group of six will receive one sentence. (If the class is not divisible into sixes, you may have to use a seventh sentence for some groups.)

This activity should be used with a class that has worked together over a period of time and where members already demonstrate respect for each other. To share feelings rather than knowledge requires a high level of trust, so friendship or pupil-selected groups may be best here.

Objectives

- to demonstrate that pupils may share common worries which can be articulated within a trusting environment

Materials

A set of *Sometimes I worry about* . . . sentences for each group (one sentence per pupil)
Pencils

Procedure

a Ask pupils to form groups of six. Give one member of each group a set of sentences and ask him not to look at any of them; he deals a sentence to each member.
b Each pupil considers his sentence alone and thinks about the feelings of the person who wrote the sentence. Invite each pupil to take the role of the writer and to be prepared, in five minutes, to describe his feelings to the group.
c Each person has two minutes in which to describe his feelings about the sentence. When he has finished, other group members describe their own feelings.
(A simple intervention, for example, 'Right, thank you number 1, now let's hear from number 2' should be sufficient to ensure that a smooth flow is maintained.)
d When all pupils within a group have contributed, this part of the activity is concluded.
e Ask pupils with the same sentence number to form new groups – ie all pupils who have 'sentence 1' will work together, and so on.
f Pupils discuss and exchange their feelings about the common sentence. (5 minutes)
g Pupils return to their original group. Without identifying the source they report back in turn (from 1 to 6) on the responses of other pupils who have been working with the same question.

Prompts for reflection

- If I have a worry I go to . . .
- I never worry about . . .
- I feel free of worries when . . .
- Today, I learnt that . . .

Suggestions for follow-up work

1 Invite pupils to compare their worries with other contemporaries or members of a different age group – using the proforma to collect information, or devising a new scheme. Does anonymity influence a person's response? How should the group gather, collate, analyse and present the data?
2 This activity may have generated a rather gloomy atmosphere. An investigation focused upon happiness 'I always feel happy when . . .' is a good follow-up.

Sometimes I worry about . . .

CHOICES

1 Sometimes I worry about . . .

2 Sometimes I worry about . . .

3 Sometimes I worry about . . .

4 Sometimes I worry about . . .

5 Sometimes I worry about . . .

6 Sometimes I worry about . . .

3.7 The magic box tells me

This activity has been adapted from 'The Magic Box' which appears in: *100 Ways to enhance self-concept in the classroom*, J. Cranfield and H.C. Wells, (New Jersey, Prentice-Hall, 1972).

Self-concept is the product of how we see ourselves and how we perceive others as seeing us. Although the mirror only provides information on reflection, it may stimulate thoughts about the image we transmit to other people. Self-esteem or a feeling of self worth is closely related to self-concept and in this activity pupils are invited to consider both features.

In the hustle and bustle of school life, pupils are rarely provided with opportunities, within the formal curriculum, to consider seriously their strengths and talents. The messages of the hidden curriculum may positively or negatively affect their self-esteem, as do situations within the formal curriculum where a pupil comes face-to-face with success or failure.

This activity is designed to provide an occasion for the pupil to think of himself as a Very Important Person (VIP) – in terms of his own self-esteem and in relation to others.

The 'magic box' in this activity consists simply of a mirror placed in a box. (See Figure 3.e)

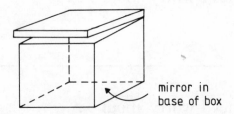

mirror in
base of box

1 To assist handling, the box should have a hinged lid.
2 An ideal size for the mirror is 10cm × 10cm. In any case it should be the exact size of the base of the box; if smaller it needs to be fixed securely to the bottom.
3 The deeper the box the better, so that the person sitting next to the user cannot easily see inside.

Figure 3.e Magic Box

Objectives

- to focus upon the individual as a very important person
- to gain insights into the feelings of other people

Materials

One magic box (see Figure 3.e) for every 6–8 pupils
Pencils
One *VIP* sentence completion slip for each pupil
A4 lined paper

Procedure

a Invite the class to give the names of people whom they consider to be VIPs (very important people). The names are recorded on the blackboard or a large sheet of paper. Pupils will probably suggest celebrities – it is less likely that anyone in the class will see himself or a classmate in this category. However, if the name of a person in the class is mentioned it should be recorded without further comment. The names remain on display throughout the session.

b Explain that within each magic box there is some information about a very important person. Emphasise that every person in the room will have an opportunity to look into one of the boxes. It is important to establish the ground rules of this exercise in order to maximise the effect: at no time should a pupil communicate with another pupil about the contents of the box; before passing it to another member of the group he should close the lid of the box; the box should only be passed to the next person when you say 'change'.

c Ask pupils to create self-selected groups of 6–8 members, so that friends work together. Members sit in a circle with one chair's width between each person.

d Hand a box to one pupil in each circle and ask him not to open it until asked to do so. (It may be necessary to reiterate the ground rules at this stage.)

e The first person looks into the box (2–3 seconds) until you say 'change'. The box is then passed to the pupil on the right. This procedure continues until all group members have looked into the box.

f Give a VIP sentence slip to each group member and ask him to complete it in private. (You may need to help some pupils do this.)

g On completion, pupils place their slips face downwards in the centre of the circle. One member shuffles the slips, and places them in a pile.

h Starting with the person to the right of the shuffler, a slip is drawn and read out to the group. The reader attempts to interpret the feelings of the writer. It is possible that the reader may draw his own slip, but he should not reveal this fact. The next person to the right draws a slip and repeats the procedure. If the reader is embarrassed or unable to offer an interpretation you may invite the group to offer an opinion.

i When each member of the group has participated, groups exchange slips and repeat the procedure. Since the pupils will now be more familiar with the procedure, they may have greater confidence and offer more detailed insights.

j Within groups, pupils discuss what constitutes a VIP. They are asked to use these criteria at home, when looking at articles and photographs in magazines and journals. An opportunity for report-back and the adjustment of criteria should be provided during the next lesson.

Prompts for reflection

- The most important thing I have learned is . . .
- A very important person is someone who . . .
- Everyone is important because . . .
- I am important to my friends because . . .
- My friends are important because . . .

Suggestions for follow-up work

1 Ask each pupil to bring three photographs from magazines or newspapers, which show a VIP. In small groups, pupils place the photographs on a table and in turns, take the role of one of the characters. In role, the pupil describes the advantages and disadvantages he feels in being considered a VIP.

2 This activity may encourage pupils to seek an interview with a VIP either by visiting him or by inviting him into school (see details of 'Receiving a visitor', page 28).

CHOICES

VIP

When I saw that the very important
person was me, I felt . . .

3.8 I am . . .

As members of a class grow in confidence and trust, they may be prepared to engage in self-disclosure. However, you should remember that there is no intrinsic virtue in encouraging pupils to 'tell all' – in some cases this may cause immediate or subsequent anguish and pain. The only justification for providing opportunities for self-disclosure lies in its potential to enhance greater self-awareness and personal growth.

Objective

- to increase confidence in discussing one's feelings with another person

Materials

One copy of *Form A* (page 74) for each pupil
Copies of *Form B* and *C* (according to the number of boys and girls in the class)
Pencils

Procedure

a Give each pupil a copy of *Form A* and invite him to underline those statements which most aptly describe him, working privately. Explain that pupils may write one, two or three additional statements in order to build a self-profile. (5–10 minutes)
b Ask pupils to select a partner. (In instances where there is an odd number in the class, a group of three is permissible.)
c Give each pupil a copy of either Form B or Form C according to whether his partner is male or female. (Where there are three members of a group, only one form is completed for *one* of the partners.)
d On the form, pupils underline those statements which best describe their partner and add one, two or three statements to complete the profile. There should be no talking at this stage. (5–10 minutes)

e Explain that each person will have the opportunity to describe how he sees himself to his partner. The partner may offer observations from *Form B* or *C* during the disclosure. At no stage will partners exchange forms; all information has to be communicated verbally. Make it clear that pupils should not feel under pressure to make statements that are likely to cause embarrassment to themselves or their partners.

f Using the underlined statements from *Form A* or his own words, one of the pair discloses his self-profile. His partner listens and comments, if appropriate. You may need to help pupils where the dialogue is proving difficult and to reiterate the ground rules for the activity. (5–10 minutes) (Where there are three pupils working together, the time per pupil may be shortened to ensure that they finish at the same time as those working in pairs.)

g The partner now discloses his self-profile and the first pupil listens and comments, if appropriate. (5–10 minutes)

h You should not repeat any part of the dialogue, nor invite pupils to recall aspects of their discussion. It is important that pupils see that you respect the privacy of pupil exchanges.

i In small groups pupils focus upon the learning experience offered by the activity.

Prompts for reflection

- The best thing about this session was . . .
- When talking about myself, I feel . . .
- A good friend is someone who . . .
- Listening to someone talking about me is . . .

Suggestions for follow-up work

Invite the class to think of ways in which a person may describe himself to others, apart from through the spoken word or by his immediate behaviour. Some suggestions might include: collage; drama; drawing; music; painting; poetry; writing.

Form A

I am happy. I am weak. I am friendly. I am a good worker. I am funny. I am strong. I am good looking. I am fit. I am sad. I am lazy.

> I am . . .
>
> I am . . .
>
> I am . . .

- ✂

Form B

He is happy. He is weak. He is friendly. He is a good worker. He is funny. He is strong. He is good looking. He is fit. He is sad. He is lazy.

> He is . . .
>
> He is . . .
>
> He is . . .

- ✂

Form C

She is happy. She is weak. She is friendly. She is a good worker. She is funny. She is strong. She is good looking. She is fit. She is sad. She is lazy.

> She is . . .
>
> She is . . .
>
> She is . . .

3.9 Another brick in the wall

This activity may prove useful at the end of a course, term or year when pupils have established working relationships. It focuses upon the positive attributes, qualities and skills of each pupil, as perceived by other class members.

In everyday life we receive both positive and negative comments from those with whom we live and work. Positive feedback – sometimes referred to as 'strokes' – enhances our self-esteem or feeling of self-worth.

In any class there are occasions when individuals and groups fall out of favour with each other, but issues are usually amicably resolved and 'forgotten'. However, some disputes are deep-rooted and tensions persist from lesson to lesson. Against this backdrop we need to develop the positive, pleasurable aspect of pupil interaction within the class and to encourage the supportive behaviour of pupils for each other.

A great deal has been written about the negative effects of 'peer group pressure' upon the behaviour of young people. However, less attention has been paid to the potential of this phenomenon when used to promote positive attitudes and behaviours. Initially a pupil may feel embarrassed when looking at his 'positive' self, but such short-lived discomfort may be justifiable because of the increased confidence that may accrue. For the person who repeatedly receives negative messages from a range of sources, this may be the first or a rare occasion when he experiences praise or even positive recognition. At times, the disorientation may give rise to tears!.

Objectives

- to provide an occasion for each pupil to receive complimentary comments from his peers
- to ensure that each pupil recognises that he has attributes, qualities and skills that are valued by his peers

Materials

One copy of *The wall* for each pupil (page 78)
Pencils

Procedure

a Invite existing work groups of fours and threes to join up into groups of eight or nine members.

b Ask the group to sit in a circle and give each pupil a copy of *The Wall* sheet on which he writes his name.

c Each pupil passes his sheet to the person sitting on his right.

d Explain that we all thrive on the positive comments (or 'strokes') that we receive from others.

e Ask each pupil to write a positive comment about the person named on the sheet in one of the 'bricks' on the 'Wall'. Individual words, phrases or sentences may be used. (You could ask the class to suggest examples to illustrate how a brick may be completed.)

f It is important that sheets are not passed to the next person until a brick on each wall has been completed. You may need to monitor what is being recorded to ensure that *only* positive comments appear in the bricks, and to remind pupils not to copy each other's comments relating to a particular person. (A minimum of 10 minutes will be necessary for this part of the activity.)

g After each group member has written something, sheets are returned to their 'owners'. Each subject thus receives a wall that contains seven or eight complimentary comments.

h Ask the pupil to write '1' and '2' in two of the empty bricks. In brick '1' he writes how he feels about the comments and in brick '2', he records attributes, qualities and skills of which he is proud but which do not appear in any of the bricks. Finally, the pupil identifies the brick of which he is most proud.

i Give the group five to ten minutes in which to talk about the acitivity with an open agenda. You should not become involved unless the group seems to be experiencing difficulty – in which case you may use prompts to stimulate discussion.

j Ask the class if anyone would like to say anything about this activity.

Prompts for reflection

• When I read the comments I felt . . .
• Last week, I could have made someone feel good if I had . . .
• I cannot always expect people to say pleasant things to me because . . .
• I think I need to behave positively towards . . .

Suggestions for follow-up work

1 Ask the class to consider how it can act as a 'support group' to all its members. It may be that the group only works together for a few lessons each week and does not see itself as a major reference group for all pupils. However, if it is a form or tutor group, it is likely to have a life over weeks, months and years.
2 Groups could develop a 'positive help' contract through brainstorming and subsequently through negotiation, focusing on ways in which they contract to help each other within and/or outside of school.

The Wall

CHOICES

Name . . . .

4 Changes

When people are asked what changes have most affected their lives the variation in responses can be startling: the death of a friend, the birth of a child, learning to drive, stopping smoking . . . the list is virtually endless. But focusing on one particularly memorable change takes attention away from the reality that our lives are filled with change. Indeed, to some extent success in life may be a function of our ability to cope with change. This notion of 'coping' with change might suggest that the process lies outside our control, as if we are constantly reacting to external forces. In fact we are equally involved in the process of initiating change. We are a force for change in ourselves – having a new hair style or joining a club – and in others – the effect of the new hair style on those who know us, or the results of joining a club for the other members.

The impact of change often evokes strong feelings. When we master a new skill – eg swimming for the first time – we feel very good, we have a positive view of ourselves. But change can also foster negative emotions. New systems, new locations or new ideas imposed upon us can cause anxiety, conflict and stress both for those affected by the changes and those who propose them. Under these circumstances we lose confidence, we doubt our abilities and if not helped our personal performance may be impaired.

The balance of positive and negative feelings about change seems to relate to the extent to which we are part of the overall process. If we are merely the passive recipients of imposed change our feelings tend to be negative. When we are partners in the process our self-esteem suffers less damage because we feel that we have a stake in it; we are part of the control, even if only a small part.

Because so much in our day to day life remains unchanged – the recurring seasons, eating and sleeping, our regular daily routine – we sometimes fail to see change around us. But, despite the constants of life through many generations, change is with us all the time. We have only to listen to older people talking, to look at old photographs or watch old newsreel footage, to realise this.

These general points about change are particularly relevant for young people to consider. In their lives they experience dramatic patterns of change. The physical, physiological and emotional upheavals of adolescence are among the most powerful forms of change we all have to cope with. At this age, young people are learning to cope with physical changes and are leaving behind their childhood. For the adolescent, life is changing: new friendships, new skills and interests, new concerns – all form the richness of personal experience that is the basis for pupil talk. The activities are merely a means to an end; their main aim is to improve the quality of pupil-pupil interaction.

The activities listed may be used independently or as part of a developmental sequence. Most of them invite the students to reflect on their own lives and the changes they have experienced. *Changing faces* takes a different slant and focuses on how we communicate feelings through changing facial expression. *Who said that?* introduces the idea of changing meanings according to whom a particular saying is attributed. Finally the activity *Changes* invites the students to look back on the whole issue of change in the form of a simple approach to peer and self-assessment.

For those who wish to spend a series of lessons on this topic, a suggested sequence of development could be: *Personal record of change, Milestones, Expectations* and *Changes quiz.* The peer and self assessment activity *Change* would then complete the sequence.

4.1 Personal record of change

Most pupils will have some form of record of their personal development. They will probably have photographs, and perhaps also sound
and video recordings, which are increasingly forming a part of family
records. Particular sensitivity will be needed if a pupil in the group is
in care or if there are adopted or fostered children in the group. Such
children may not have photographs of themselves as babies or young
children. One possibility for such pupils is to make available to them
photographs of yourself as a child or, if other members of staff are
willing, photographs of them as children.

The materials used will be precious to their owners, so considerable
preparation of the group will be necessary. It may be helpful for the
group to establish a set of ground rules to protect the materials. In any
case, you should ensure that every photograph bears the name of its
owner on the back.

The procedure calls for partners to make a list of changes they can
see in the different photographs of the person they are working with.
As with other activities in this book this may create an opportunity for
negative comments at the expense of an individual. For this reason it
is important that you are mobile and vigorous in your contact with all
the working pairs. How you deal with intentionally damaging comments will depend largely on your knowledge of the individuals
involved and the circumstances. It may be worth recalling the section
in Chapter 2 which deals with ground rules for the group (see pages
30–31) and to take time to remind the group of their existence and the
need for everyone to uphold them.

When the partners represent each other in their fours it is very
important that they speak in the first person, as if they were their
partner. This procedure may be difficult for some pupils but it is well
worth developing as a regular feature of the group's work.

Objectives

- to show that physical change takes place in all of us
- to search for patterns of similarity and difference in personal
  growth

Materials

Personal photographs from birth to the present.
A copy of the *Personal record* for each pupil
One copy of the *Patterns of change* sheet for each group
Pencils

Procedure

a Organise the class into pairs and give out one *Personal Record* for each pupil.
b Each pupil arranges his or her photographs into a chronological sequence.
c The sequences are exchanged between partners.
d From observing the photographs and looking at their partner as he is today, each person records on the sheet the changes they can see in their partner.
e Pairs decide who is **A** and who is **B**.
f **A** describes his observations to **B**.
g **B** describes his observations to **A**.
h The photographs are returned to their owners, who are asked to agree or disagree with their partner's observations.
i Invite pairs to join up to form groups of four. In turn each person talks *as if they were their partner* describing the changes observed from their partner's photographs.
j Distribute one copy of the *Patterns of change* sheet to each group of four. Ask groups to work out what changes they all have in common, and what things remain.
k Still working in fours, invite the groups to describe changes which cannot be seen in photographs. Make a list of these changes.

Prompts for reflection

• The main changes I noticed in *your* photographs were . . .
• What I noticed about my clothes was . . .
• What I noticed about my face was . . .
• What I noticed about my general appearance was . . .

Suggestions for follow-up work

1 Invite pupils to make a list of 10 ways in which they think they have changed. Each pupil chooses one of the ways and describes the changes in some detail. Pupils could show their results to parents or someone who knows them well, to see if they agree.
2 Pupils could compare their photographs with old photographs (borrowed from grandparents, elderly relatives or neighbours). Apart from the differences in clothing and surroundings, what other differences and similarities are there in the two sets of photographs? Do the older people agree about these?

CHOICES

Personal record

Observer's name _____

Partner's name _____

Changes noted

1 _____

2 _____

3 _____

4 _____

5 _____

6 _____

7 _____

8 _____

Patterns of change

CHOICES

Names of group members —————————————— date ————————

things that change	things that don't change	changes which can't be seen

4.2 So who's this?

As with *Personal record of change* this relies upon pupils being able to provide a photograph of themselves when younger. It is advisable to have some extra photographs available – perhaps of other members of staff, if they are willing to contribute. If these are used it will, however, change the nature of the activity – unless they can be persuaded to join the group and take part. The purpose of the activity is to focus attention on the changes which growth brings yet at the same time to reinforce the idea that we each have a unique set of features which form the basis of our physical individuality.

It may be necessary to state a fixed time after which those who have not identified the people in their photographs should make them available for the whole group to work on. This activity requires freedom of movement by pupils. It can result in a lot of noise and it is intended to be fun as well as a learning experience. Ideally it should take place in a large, open space.

Ensure that any family photographs brought in by the class can be clearly identified by their owners.

Figure 4.a shows the rules for the activity, which should be established at the start.

---

1 No-one is allowed to challenge a potential owner without using preliminary questions.
2 Statements or questions must be based on observations of the photographs and/or the person spoken to.
3 Preliminary statements should be of the kind – 'The person in this photograph, like you, has curly hair, dark eyes and she is a girl. Did you ever visit a park like the one shown here?' or 'I see that you have blonde hair, parted on the right and that your chin is quite pointed like the person in this photograph. Did you ever wear a blue jumper like this one?'
4 Once the person is sure that they have found the owner of the picture they may then say 'Is the person in this picture you?'
5 Once the owner is found the picture is returned to him/her and the observer should sit down in a prominent place to show he/she is available for questioning.

Fig. 4.a   Rules for the activity

Objectives

- to promote close observation
- to show that although we change as we grow, we retain some unchanging features

Materials

Enough envelopes for one per pupil, plus the teacher
  (each envelope should have a number clearly written inside the flap)
A personal photograph from early childhood for each pupil

Procedure

a Explain the rules for the activity (Figure 4.a).
b Give out the numbered envelopes.
c Ask each pupil to memorise the number of their envelope and place their photograph inside it, but not to seal the flap.
d Pupils rapidly exchange envelopes for about 30 seconds, after which each pupil should have a numbered envelope they do not recognise.
e Pupils take out the photographs and find out who they belong to (see Figure 4.a, *Rules*).
f It may be necessary to stop this activity before all the photographs have been matched against their owners. In this case, ask the class to sit together in a cluster. Those who have not yet had their photograph returned form a line along one wall. Those who have been unable to identify the owner of their photographs form a line opposite the first one. As a group, pupils now attempt to match the photographs to faces. When the group is satisfied that they are correct they take it in turns to challenge a member of the line.

Prompts for reflection

In pairs:
- The most difficult part of the activity for me was . . .
- I had to laugh when . . .
- I was so sure that the photograph I had was . . .
- If I was doing this activity again I . . .

Suggestions for follow-up work

1 Invite pupils to search out old school photographs from primary school days and see how many people they can name, writing the names on the back of the photograph or on a sheet of paper.
2 Pupils could ask older relatives or neighbours if they have old school photographs, preferably group or class photographs. 'Ask them to name people on the photographs who you also know. Do you recognise them? How are we able to recognise people from their photographs after many years?'

Supplementary activities using photographs

In all these activities you will need to give special consideration to the feelings of adopted and fostered children or those from single-parent families, who may not be able to obtain photographs of relatives.

A   Ask the pupils to bring in photographs of their brothers, sisters and parents taken at about the same age.
Arrange the parent photographs into a set and display the set with a number against each photograph. Repeat this for all the other photographs, taking care not to put family sets together.
Now challenge the class, working in pairs, to find the family sets, starting with the brothers/sisters, and then matching these with the mothers/fathers. Pairs could discuss:
● What I noticed about the family group was . . .
● The main differences I could see were . . .
● What I feel about this activity is . . .

B   Ask the pupils to bring current photographs of their parents/ grandparents and photographs of the same people as children. Display the photographs at random, each one clearly numbered. Challenge the pupils, working in pairs, to match as many photographs as possible, making notes on the reasons for their choice. After sufficient time for all pairs to have had some success, combine pairs to form fours. In fours, pupils compare their results. Now give out a list of numbers for the true matches and leave time for everyone to check these against the photographs. Pairs could discuss:
● The main changes I noticed were . . .
● The features which helped me to match up pictures were . . .

4.3 50 ways we've changed

Brainstorming is a way of quickly collecting many ideas that can be offered by everyone in a group. Because there are no right or wrong answers everyone is free to contribute. (See Chapter 2, page 30 for details on how to use brainstorming.)

Although the title of this activity is *50 ways we've changed* you should be prepared to accept more or fewer ideas than this.

The most difficult stage in the process is deciding on the categories for change. You may have to help the group to see all of the common patterns, if they are struggling. When picking out the categories it is a good idea to use coloured chalk or felt-tip pens to underline associated suggestions in a single colour.

Objectives

- to categorise the different ways in which we change

Materials

Blackboard and chalk or flip chart and pens (newsprint and thick felt-tip pens are just as good)
One copy of the *50 ways we've changed* sheet for each pupil
Coloured pens or pencils

Procedure

a Work with the whole class, using the 'brainstorming' technique.
b When their ideas have been collected, go through the list and group words into categories of change, eg physical change, interests, likes/dislikes . . .
c Hand out copies of the *50 ways we've changed* sheet and invite pupils to write the titles of the agreed categories in the appropriate spaces
d Each person writes the personal changes they see in themselves in each category box that applies to them. Where no change has occurred, they should note how they are the same.
e Pupils work in pairs to compare lists.

Prompts for reflection

- To me the most surprising way I have changed in the last few years is . . .
- I hadn't readily noticed, but *you've* changed too, I remember when . . .

Suggestions for follow-up work

1 Pupils could have a conversation with the oldest person they find it easy to talk with, about the work on change, asking them 'What are the three most impressive changes you have seen in your life? What three things have not changed in the same period?'
Pupils list the impressive changes and the things that have not changed and build up a class list for each over a period of a few weeks. How much is there in common between different people's lists?
2 Introduce an enquiry with something like: 'Today many of us wear digital watches; we tell the time by patterns of numbers displayed on a small screen. It may surprise you but had you been able to show your watch to the first man to fly in space the astronaut would not have immediately recognised what it was; he certainly would not know how to operate its different functions. Can you think of any other startling developments that have produced change in our lives; new inventions, new equipment, new ideas? Bring these ideas to class and build up a list.'

50 ways we've changed

CATEGORY 1

CATEGORY 2

CATEGORY 3

CATEGORY 4

CATEGORY 5

4.4 Changing faces

Though words may express what is in our minds our faces normally display what we *feel*. Extremes of feeling, as represented in facial expressions, are usually unmistakeable and it is important that we learn to interpret these accurately. The purpose of this activity is to explore the connection between feelings and facial expressions. Pupils are encouraged to note the changes that we make to the shape of our mouth and the outlook of our eyes when representing specific feelings.

A good way to start off this particular activity is with a display of newspaper photographs showing different facial expressions – the elated goal scorer, the golfer who has missed a put, the worried politician, the proud parents . . . and invite the class to say what they think each person was feeling. This kind of beginning allows the class to formulate a vocabulary of terms that will be particularly useful to the less articulate.

This activity is limited in that it relies on the person with the card to be able to represent the feeling accurately, and also requires the person seeing the facial expression to have the vocabulary to describe it accurately. Despite this limitation, the activity is worthwhile and can promote considerable discussion within a group. At the end of the activity there are suggestions for an alternative way of working for less articulate individuals.

Objectives

• to explore the connection between feelings and facial expression

Materials

A set of *Prompt cards* (page 95) for each pair
An envelope for each pair
One *Recording sheet* per pupil
Pencils

Procedure

a Organise the class into pairs.

b Give each pair one set of prompt cards in an envelope, and one recording sheet for each person.

c Explain that the pupils in each pair should observe each other's faces in silence for ten seconds.

d Pupils decide who will be **A** and who **B** in each pair.

e Person **A** takes one prompt card from the envelope. Without letting **B** see the word, he or she copies it into the top box in the column marked 'prompt word' on the recording sheet. The card is not returned to the envelope but hidden from view.

f Person **A** now depicts the meaning of the word by a facial expression. **B** then writes down what he thinks was on the card in the top box in the column marked 'response'.

g **A** and **B** now compare the word on the card with the written response.

h **A** passes the envelope to **B**, who takes out a card and repeats the procedure.

i The envelope is passed backwards and forwards until all the word cards are used up.

j **A** and **B** compare their recording sheets to see how accurate their interpretation of the facial expressions has been.

k Pairs combine to form groups of four to compare results and discuss the activity.

Prompts for reflection

- The words I found most difficult to interpret were . . .
- The words I found easiest to interpret were . . .
- I can always tell when someone feels . . . because their face is like . . .
- When I'm . . . my face is always like . . .
- I can tell when you're . . . because you look like . . .

Suggestions for follow-up work

Pupils could extend their observations to the world beyond the classroom in a public place such as the school dining room, the playground, a supermarket or bus station, watching people's facial expressions as they go about their business, have a conversation, play, rest etc . . ..

An alternative way of working

Instead of writing out the word that the observer thinks is being represented the facial expression can also be recorded in pictorial form. Pupils can produce a stylised expression by drawing in the shape and position of the mouth, eyebrows and nose on blank outline of faces like the one below. For example, surprised or worried faces might look like these:

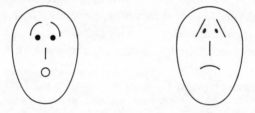

The advantage of this approach lies in the freedom it gives to those pupils whose lack of facility with language does not allow them to translate into words what they can see expressed in someone's face.

Changing faces prompt cards

happy	sad
angry	anxious
frightened	excited
fed-up	uninterested
jealous	worried

Changing faces
recording sheet

CHOICES

prompt word	response
1	
2	
3	
4	
5	
6	
7	
8	
9	
10	

4.5 Expectations

As we grow older our expectations of ourselves and others change. Young girls and boys who play together at the age of five may not wish to be near each other under any circumstances at the age of ten. In a related way the expectations others have of us also change – we may get away with being irresponsible when we are young but before long people will point out that we are getting old enough to know better!

This activity focuses on the issue of expectations: things we expected of ourselves, expectations others had of us or we had of them. Though most young people can quite accurately recall childhood memories they may need help in identifying and describing the expectations they had of themselves. The following prompts may be useful:

- Did you help out in the house?
- Did you look after any pets?
- Were you allowed to go to the shops/town alone?
- Who decided when it was time to go to bed?
- Who decided how you spent your pocket money?

Although the procedure is quite complicated this activity can work very well if a supportive atmosphere is established. Because the method requires individuals to write about their partners it is most productive if they know each other well. This may result in some members new to the group being without a partner. It is important to encourage such members to work together and to give them extra support.

If you intend to pick up points from individuals for public discussion make sure they are happy about this. It can be helpful to run through the content of the point as a kind of rehearsal before they speak publicly.

Objectives

- to explore the changing expectations we have of ourselves as we grow
- to explore the changing expectations others have of us as we grow

Materials

A copy of the *Expectations* booklet (pages 100–101) for each pupil
Pencils

Procedure

a Invite each pupil to find a partner – someone they have known for a long time. Pupils who have come to the school more recently could be paired together and helped to use the prompts in a personally reflective way.
b Ask partners to talk about times when they were younger, to bring back memories from their earlier years. (5 minutes) Ensure both partners have a chance to talk about themselves before writing in the booklets.
c Hand out the *Expectations* booklets. Each pupil writes their partner's name on the cover.
d Pairs use the prompts on page 1 of the booklet as a basis for a conversation. (5 minutes)
e Each then writes his or her partner's comments into the booklet. (2 minutes)
f Pupils turn to the next section of the booklet. The same procedure is repeated for the remaining sections until all sections are complete.
g After completion invite the pupils to exchange booklets and read their partner's comments.
h Still in pairs, pupils discuss the exercise.

Prompts for reflection

- Looking back, the funniest thing I was expected to do was . . .
- The most annoying thing I was expected to do was . . .
- The thing that surprised me most about what you expected of yourself was . . .
- The most satisfying expectation I fulfilled was . . .

Suggestions for follow-up work

1 The activity *Milestones* could follow on from this.
2 Ask pupils to project themselves forwards to a time when they have

children of the age they are now. 'What do you think their expectations of you as their parent might be? Make a list. How does your list compare with the expectations you now have of your parents?'

3 Alternatively, pupils could look forward to the time when they are 18. 'What expectations for yourself do you have between now and then? Make a list. Share your list with a friend and make comparisons.'

Expectations

1

Partner's name _____
What is your partner's earliest memory of childhood?
_____

How old was he/she at the time? _____
Who else is involved in the memory? _____
What were they doing? _____
At this age what kind of things was he/she expected to do for him/herself? _____
_____

At the same age what was he/she *not* expected to do?
_____

You may want to add some questions of your own, write these and your partner's answers on the back of this sheet.

- ✂

2

Add 3 years to your partner's age at their earliest memory.
How old would this make your partner? _____
What kind of things did your partner do at this age?
_____

What jobs did he/she do in the home? _____
How did he/she spend most of his/her time? _____
_____

What new things was he/she expected to do? _____
_____

Add your own extra questions and your partner's answers on the back of this sheet.

3

Now come to the present time. What is your partner's age? _____

How does your partner spend his/her time out of school? _____

What jobs is he/she expected to do? _____

What is he/she really good at? _____
What would he/she like to be good at? _____
What do other people expect of him/her? _____

What does he/she expect of him/herself? _____

Put your own questions and answers on the back of this sheet.

- ✂-

4

Add another 5 years to your partner's present age.
What would your partner most like to be doing in 5 years time? _____

Where would he/she like to be? _____
Does he/she expect to achieve this? _____
What things need to happen to make this expectation become real? _____

What is your expectation of your partner? _____

What is your partner's expectation of you? _____

4.6 Milestones

Our lives are filled with experiences and some of them have a major effect on us. For young people such important happenings may occur quite frequently since so many of their experiences are new to them. This activity invites individuals to look back on their lives and pick out events or experiences that are important enough to stand out like milestones.

The *Milestones* checksheet (page 104) has a long list of potentially milestone-like events but this list should not be used if the group can produce their own. For the first ten minutes individuals are asked to work alone, however the value of the work is in discussing with a partner particular events which stand out in the memory.

It is important that you move around the class throughout this activity and are particularly sensitive to group members who may be focusing on sad events which formed milestones in their lives.

The connection between this work and that done in the previous activity *Expectations* forms a rich basis for further discussion in the group.

Objectives

- to reflect on personal development and identify points at which our lives change

Materials

A copy of the *Milestones* checksheet for each pupil
Pencils

Procedure

a Organise the class into self-selected pairs. (It may be necessary to allow groups of three but at this stage avoid larger groupings.)
b Give out the *Milestones* checksheets.
c Without any discussion between partners, individuals fill in their own checksheets, adding milestones of their own choice.

d When partners have completed their sheets invite them to exchange sheets and read each other's comments.
e Allow time for discussion and comparisons in pairs.
f Using the information in the *Expectations* booklet (see previous activity) and the *Milestones* checklist, build up a picture of changes that have occurred in members of the class.

Suggestions for follow-up work

1 Brainstorm with the class 'milestones' they have yet to come to in their lives. Ask pairs to choose one item each from the brainstorm and work out the changes that will occur when they have passed their chosen milestones.
2 Produce a time-line for the class since it came together at the start of the first year. Highlight the main changes that have taken place in the life of the class.

Milestones checksheet

CHOICES

1 I was _____ when I had my first pet. The difference it made to me was _____

2 I was _____ when I learned to ride a bicycle. The difference it made to me was _____

3 I was _____ when I read my first book. The difference it made to me was _____

4 I was _____ when I learned to swim. The difference it made to me was _____

5 I was _____ when I first climbed a tree. The difference it made to me was _____

6 I was _____ when I had my first fight. The difference it made to me was _____

7 I was _____ when I first played in a team. The difference it made to me was _____

8 I was _____ when I had my first boy/girlfriend. The difference it made to me was _____

9 I was _____ when I can remember feeling very sad. The difference it made to me was _____

10 I was _____ when I can remember feeling very happy. The difference it made to me was _____

add some **MILESTONES** of your own

4.7 Who said that?

We all tend to have strong views about particular topics and people. These views may be based on feelings of agreement or disagreement but in either case we will have certain expectations, perhaps about spoken comments or a series of events. When the comments or events fit these expected patterns our views are reinforced and we may fail to question the validity of what we are condoning or condemning. If there is a mismatch between what happens and our expectations we may be confused. At this moment of confusion the extent to which we are prepared to accommodate the discrepancy is a reflection of our independence of thought and our ability to make choices.

This issue of independence of thought is important to young people. They are at a stage when the peer group plays an important part in the lives of individuals. When an individual who we expect to behave well is drawn into a pattern of group misbehaviour we despair. How many teachers, in a moment of exasperation, have sarcastically reacted with such words as ' . . . and if they walked under a bus would you follow them there too?'. This particular activity takes up the issue of how our perceptions are influenced by individuals.

Objectives

- to explore the things that cause us to change our views
- to investigate how far our view of a person influences our perceptions of what that person says

Materials

Sets of *Who said that?* statement cards in sealed envelopes – one statement card plus one occupation card (page 106) for each group

Procedure

a Ask the class to form groups of four.
b Give each group a set of statement cards in a sealed envelope.

c The groups open the envelopes and take it in turns to read the statement aloud.

d Visit each group to explain the inclusion of a particular occupation in their envelope. Do not reveal that each group has a different named occupation.

e Invite the class to decide individually if they agree or disagree with the attributed statement.

f Create an imaginary continuum line across the classroom with 'strongly agree' at one end and 'strongly disagree' at the other.

g Invite pupils to take up a position on the line appropriate to their own feeling.

h Read out the statement again so that pupils can confirm their chosen position. Following any changes, ask each person in turn to say which person they were told had made the statement originally.

i Tell the class that the statement was made up by the authors of the book. Check to see if anyone would like to change their position.

(This procedure can be repeated with a second statement but is probably more effectively dealt with through a debriefing session.)

Prompts for reflection

• When I learned that the statement was made up by the authors of the book I . . .
• If I have made up my mind about something and then the situation changes I . . .
• The things which cause me to change my mind are . . .

Suggestions for follow-up work

1 Provide a range of newspapers for one day. Groups of three or four select a newspaper and go through it together. Invite each group in turn to identify a particular major story of that day. The other groups search for the same story, comparing not only the form of treatment and degree of coverage but also the page on which it appeared.

  Pupils cut out the topics and paste them on to pieces of sugar paper to form a display. Highlight those aspects of the treatment of the stories which make them different. 'How does the treatment change our views of the issues?'

2 Provide the class with sets of ten related pictures – ideally, photographs of the school and the local community, including shots of
individuals or groups behaving in a variety of ways – all part of a
sequence representing a particular event or situation. In groups of
four or five invite the pupils to choose no more than six pictures and
arrange them into a sequence to make a story. When groups have
agreed on their stories invite each in turn to display their chosen
sequence and tell their version of the story. Finally, discuss how the
story changes according to the choices made by the group.

4.8 Changes quiz

We live our lives as members of various groups. For most people the family forms an immediate group as does the circle of friends and acquaintances with whom we choose to spend our leisure time. Sometimes the groups to which we belong provide only occasional contact, other groups completely surround us, even to the extent of becoming an all-powerful force in our lives.

The members of a group have a variety of common interests or experiences; these are the things which bind the group together. One aspect of this 'glue' of belonging is the extent to which individuals are aware of each other in terms of personal interests, needs and changes.

This particular activity focuses on our awareness of changes. The class are asked to produce a collection of personal statements, written individually and independently, which form the basis for sharing information and feelings about personal changes.

Objectives

- to increase personal awareness within the group of pupils
- to share information within the group

Materials

One A5 piece of paper for each member of the class
Pencils

Procedure

a Invite the class to divide into pairs.
b Pairs talk about changes that they have seen around the school or in the local community. (5 minutes) (If other activities in this section have been used, remind the group of the different aspects of change that have been covered.)
c Pupils work independently for three minutes while they think about particular changes in their own lives. Areas where they might recognise change in themselves include: appearance, personal

performance in school work or in sport, friendship patterns, membership of clubs or societies, eating habits etc.

d Ask each pupil to write about one recent change in his life (using the paper provided) (3 minutes). Make sure everyone understands that the written comments will be read out to the whole class.

e Fold up all the pieces of paper and put them into a bag.

f One person (or you) reads out a piece of writing and the class has to identify who wrote the particular statement.

Prompts for reflection

For small groups, up to four people:
• The one that gave me most difficulty was . . .
• I chose my particular change because . . .
• The things I didn't realise about . . .

Suggestions for follow-up work

The previous activity can be adapted by inviting pupils to describe changes they have seen in others rather than in themselves. It is important to stress the use of *positive* comments and to ensure that this is adhered to. Two ways in which this can be done are as follows:

1 Invite each person to choose one other person in the class and, without identifying this person, describe in writing one *positive* way in which they have changed. These statements can either be put into a bag and drawn out at random, or each person in turn can read out their statement for the class to decide who it belongs to.

2 Provide each person with a piece of A4 paper, either pinned to their back or attached to a clip board. Individuals are invited to contribute *positive* comments to each other describing ways in which the other has changed.

4.9 Change

This activity is intended to round off the series of activities in this section on change. Where a number of activities have been used in sequence this one will help pupils to draw together the experience and evaluate the work and the part they have played within it. A booklet of prompts is a simple and cost-effective device to produce but a powerful one to use (see pages 113–116). Eventually the pupils themselves should be able to produce the prompts to go in the booklet.

Objectives

- to promote sensitivity and support in the group
- to look back on the work undertaken on 'Changes'

Materials

Class set of *Changes* prompt booklet (see pages 113–116)

Procedure

a Invite the class to arrange themselves in pairs.
b Hand out the *Changes* prompt booklets.
c Partners decide who will be **A** and **B**.
d **A** opens the booklet at page 1 and reads out the first prompt (see Fig. 4.b). The booklet is passed backwards and forwards between **A** and **B** until all the prompts have been dealt with.
e Complete the work with a class discussion reflecting back on the work undertaken on the topic 'change'.

Suggestions for follow-up work

Invite pupils to devise a different set of prompts to focus discussion on changes that individuals would like to see in their own class. These could be pooled and displayed then put in order of importance before applying the general problem solving approach suggested earlier.

- The part of this work I liked most was . . .
- The part I liked most was . . .
- For me the least interesting part was . . .
- The part I think was least interesting was . . .
- What I learned from you while we worked together was . . .
- What I learned from you was . . .
- What I learned about the class as a whole was . . .
- What I learned about the class was . . .
- What I learned about myself was . . .
- What I learned about myself was . . .
- The change that I am most looking forward to is . . .
- The change I am looking forward to most is . . .

*Fig. 4.b. Prompts in the changes booklet (some are repeated to give the same opportunity to comment for both **A** and **B**).*

Who said that?

Statement card 1

Young people today have little enthusiasm for work!

a television personality
a footballer
a pop star
a supermarket manager
a garage owner
a head teacher

Statement card 2

When it comes to organising themselves girls are better than boys!

a female olympic runner
a female bus driver
a female politician
a male olympic coach
a male nurse
a male teacher

Making a prompt booklet

The original can be used directly with a plain paper copier or indirectly on a spirit duplicator, an ink duplicator or an offset litho press by making a master.

1. Make up a dummy booklet as described on pages 114–116.
2. Providing you use less than 16 prompts (12 are offered in Fig 4.b) only two pieces of A4 paper will be needed for each booklet.
3. Using the two pieces of paper cut along the long axis and fold the sheets into a dummy booklet.
4. Number the top corners of each sheet in order.
5. Write either the prompts in Fig 4.b or your own prompts on to the pages of the dummy. (Remember to write only one prompt on each side.)
6. Sellotape the parts together in their original positions.
7. When you are satisfied with the dummy, produce an identical set of master sheets from which to print copies.
8. Make the required number of copies for side 1.
9. Copy side 2 on to the back of the side 1 copies.
10. Repeat for the remaining two sides of the other master sheets.
11. Cut both sets of copies down the centre line of the long axis.
12. Collate the sets so that prompts are in order on the numbered sheets.
13. Fold each collated set down the centre line of the short axis.
14. Staple along the centre fold of each booklet.

You now have a set of 16-sided booklets.

The layout of pages in the changes booklet is designed to promote conversations in pairs. Only one prompt appears each time a page of the booklet is opened. In this way the booklet is passed backwards and forwards between members of each pair. This procedure for reflecting on a particular piece of work is one way of introducing the process of peer and self-assessment.

Written work can be introduced either by providing lines for written responses on each page or by inviting pupils to write their responses in the form of a self produced report. If the strategy is to be used as part of a developmental group work programme introduce the opportunity for the participants to create their own prompts. An initial stage might simply be 'A's prompt for B' and 'B's prompt for A'. The involvement of pupils in the creation of their own prompts for reflection may be built up until the only role for the teacher is the production of blank booklets. If this stage is reached the purpose of the booklet has been reduced to a device for recording, for the pupils should by then have internalised the principle as well as the process of personal reflection and peer support.

This general system for making a small booklet is very flexible. When producing a booklet first decide the number of items requiring a single side of paper in the booklet. Now decide if the front and back cover need to carry information. Count up the total number of single sides needed. Divide this number by 8. If the number is exactly divisible by 8 the number obtained is the number of A4 sheets required. If the number does not divide exactly by 8 then increase the number to the next highest number that will divide exactly by 8

    eg   A 16 sided booklet divides by 8 exactly 2 times; it will require 2 pieces of A4 to make it. A 21 sided booklet does not divide exactly by 8 so increase the number to the next highest number to divide by 8, that is 24. This gives 3 pieces of A4 paper required for a 21 sided booklet.

To work out the position of each item in the booklet first make up a dummy booklet. Place the required number of A4 sheets together and mark each sheet clearly with a large number.

Fold the sheets along the centre.

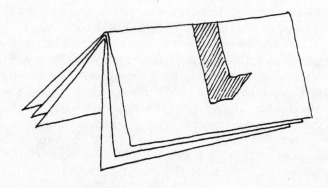

Tear along each fold to give 6 pieces of paper.

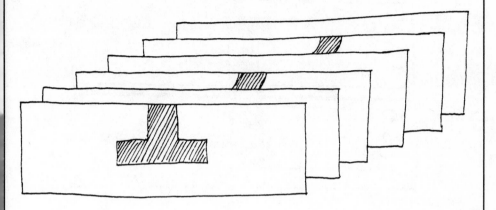

Fold the six sheets along the centre across the paper.

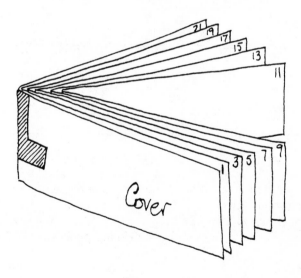

Mark up the cover and the back and number each sheet as shown above on both sides.
Reform the original A4 pieces of paper. It is helpful if the halves are sellotaped together.

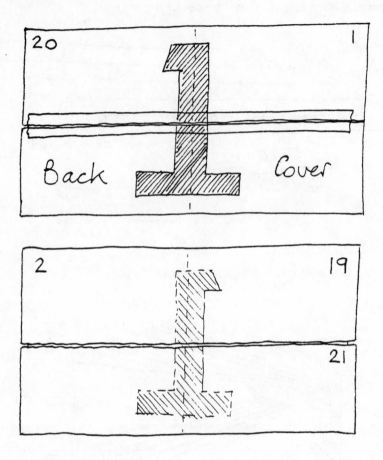

Note that the sum of the two numbers on any one piece of paper should be the same on all pieces.

Use this dummy booklet to position the individual elements of each booklet and to check the back to back printing position.

5 How others see us

How others see us is intimately and reciprocally tied up with how we see ourselves. The image we have of ourselves is made up of many interacting forces, some of which have their origins within ourselves while some come from the effects that others have upon us (see Figure 5a).

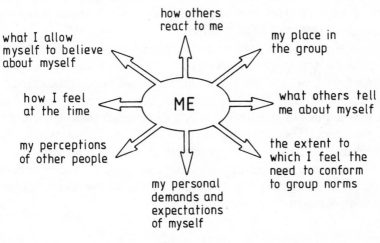

Fig. 5.a

The view that we are the products of our own experience reflects this set of interacting forces. It also assumes that we are sensitive to the world around us and capable of making sense of it in order to take it into account. When we cease to achieve this we become fixed, set in our ways and bigotted; we risk seeing others as stereotypes. We lose our capacity to accept and value differences and find it increasingly difficult to deal with change.

This chapter deals with some fundamental aspects of personal development. The activities here, as with those in all other chapters, are provided as a means to an end. They will stimulate discussion and feelings, so it is very important that the period at the end of each activity is used effectively to reflect on the experiences. This means that the pupils will not only experience the activity but also find meaning in it for themselves. Time should always be set aside for this while the class is still together.

Ideally, all the activities should be used as part of a developmental programme focusing on self. The activities *Clumps, Continua* and *Similarities/Differences* offer introductions to the notion of the acceptance of difference. They also illustrate effective ways in which groups of people can express variations in attitudes and opinions.

Wrapped objects and *Roots* offer quite different ways of introducing personal elements into discussion. The former is based on personal perceptions of something important to self; the latter offers a means of setting individuals into a common context, in this case childhood.

The activity *You and me* is probably best dealt with as an extension of the preceding work and only handled if the class has developed a supportive pattern of relationships.

Personal gifts and *Proud circle* offer opportunities for individuals to say positive things to one another. Care is needed in using these approaches. Teachers need to be sure that they and the class group can provide mutual support. The emphasis here is on *positive* statements and it is important that young people experience these both as givers and receivers. Too often we develop our capacity to take negative comments at the expense of our ability to deal with positive support. We tend to become skilled at deflecting and dismissing the attempts of others to give support – at the same time reacting like a sponge to negative comment.

5.1 Clumps

In taking young people to a position where they are able to focus their attention on themselves and others without embarrassment or destructive sarcasm it is important to start with concrete experience, through activities which are simple and achievable. *Clumps* provides clear 'evidence' of similarities and differences in the class. It allows for an initial awareness of the acceptance of difference. The pace should be fast. The activity requires ease of movement and as such is best suited to an uncluttered space.

Initial control lies with the teacher, through the choice of prompts, but the activity lends itself well to pupil control once they have got the idea. It therefore provides the learners with an opportunity to take responsibility within the group for their own learning.

The prompts included require the class either to observe closely or to question carefully. Hair colour is specifically included as the last prompt to allow the teacher an opportunity to introduce the idea of degrees of similarity/difference. This offers a clear link with the second activity *Continua*.

Objectives

- to explore similarities and differences in group members
- to look closely at each other

Materials

None

Procedure

a Clear a central space in the classroom by putting the desks and chairs to one side, or work in an open space away from the classroom.
b Invite the class to get into groups according to stated criteria. Use the following prompts to start the activity off:
  - same eye colour

- same shoe colour
- number of teeth
- older brothers and/or sisters (4 groups!)
- hair colour

c After each formation of clumps the class walks around slowly waiting for the next prompt.

d Invite members of the group to introduce their own prompts.

Prompts for reflection

- What I liked about this activity was . . .
- The similarities I have with others are . . .
- The differences between myself and others are . . .
- The feelings I have about the differences are . . .
- What I have learned is . . .

Suggestions for follow-up work

1 Invite the class to work in groups. Pupils arrange themselves in the groups either as one clump or a number of clumps without stating the criteria for their groupings. Other members of the class are then invited to join the clump with which they think they are associated. The basis of the division is then explained. This modification makes a strong connection with the activity *Similarities/Differences*.

2 Introduce the notion of sub-clumps by adding a second criterion for division once the first has been acted on, eg straight hair/curly hair followed by long hair/short hair. This can be continued until the whole class is a collection of individuals, nicely making the point that though we have so many similarities we are all different.

5.2 Continua

Differences are either clear-cut or matters of opinion. 'Blue eyes or brown eyes' as a basis of distinction is beyond debate, but *degree* of blueness or brownness will require discussion. This entire chapter is about quite fundamental similarities and differences based upon such things as attitudes, values and behaviour. But these will not be arrived at for some without a series of stepping stones to help them make the journey.

Continua marks this development from initial experiences rooted in quite clear-cut differences through to experiences based upon personal opinion and group discussion. As with *Clumps* the activity, though teacher-initiated, can easily become pupil-led. The suggestions for follow-up work describe ways in which this can be achieved.

This activity is one of a number of generic ways of working which are transferable to many situations. In this particular context the pupils physically represent their own position along the continuum. This is, in a sense, a public display and as such lends itself quite naturally to debate. The activity offers a blend of personal decision making and group interaction which provide a rich source of learning experiences.

The concept of continua can also be used in other ways. Drawn as lines on paper with the two ends identified with clear language, they allow learners to judge their own position. By keeping a record of such judgements learners can gain an overview of their own development, captured in a series of 'snapshots' of points in their achievement and progress.

Objectives

• to introduce the idea that some differences are actually variations of a similarity
• to promote group contact and close observation

Materials

None

Procedure

a Clear a space big enough to allow the whole class to stand in line side by side.
b The class lines up at random shoulder-to-shoulder across the room.
c Invite the class to rearrange themselves in the same line so that the tallest member stands at the right end, the smallest at the left, with a gradual progression in between.
d Repeat the process for hair colour, size of hand, distance to come to school, number of house etc.

Prompts for reflection

• What I noticed about my position in the line was . . .
• The main similarities and differences in this class are . . .
• The way I feel about the similarities and differences is . . .

Suggestions for follow-up work

1 Invite groups to introduce their own criteria.
2 Vary the criteria to non-visual bases for placement, eg most sporting/least sporting; most musical/least musical; most noisy/least noisy . . .
3 Invite the class to form small groups and decide upon a specific criteria for arranging their group. Without telling the class what this criteria is, the group position the whole class, including themselves, and challenge the rest to say what the criterion is.

5.3 Similarities/differences

Notes for teachers

This activity continues the sequence started by *Clumps* and *Continua*. It requires the pupils to work in quite small groups and to focus their attention specifically upon themselves. There is really only one rule for the activity – that no one should ever be left alone. The differences and similarities should always be based upon features shared by at least two people.

If the class is used to working in this way you may not feel it necessary to introduce the activity. Otherwise a 'dummy run' with the sheet of illustrations will help make the rule quite clear.

Objectives

- to focus on ways we are similar and ways we are different
- to show that it is acceptable to be different

Materials

One *Similar/Different* object sheet for each group

Procedure

a Ask the class to arrange themselves into groups of 5 or 6.
b Give out the *Similar/Different* objects sheet to each group. Ask the pupils to fold the paper and tear it into pieces, each carrying a single illustration. Each pupil takes one illustration. Demonstrate one way in which the objects (pupils) can be grouped so that no-one is left out.
c In their groups, pupils suggest other ways in which the illustrations can be divided without leaving one out.
d Collect in the pieces of paper.
e Invite the groups to decide how they can organise themselves into sub-groups. (1 minute)

f Ask each group to come forward in its sub-groups and explain the basis of the groupings to the rest of the class.

g After a number of such illustrations, invite the class to suggest how the same activity could be done differently. (See *Suggestions for follow-up work*)

Prompts for reflection

- I think the purpose of this activity is . . .
- What I have learned from this is . . .
- The most surprising part of this work for me is . . .

Suggestions for follow-up work

1 Invite the groups to challenge each other to guess the basis of their sub-groups.
2 Invite the groups to work in pairs. Each group decides how the other might be divided into sub-groups, leaving them to work out the basis of the division.

Similar/Different

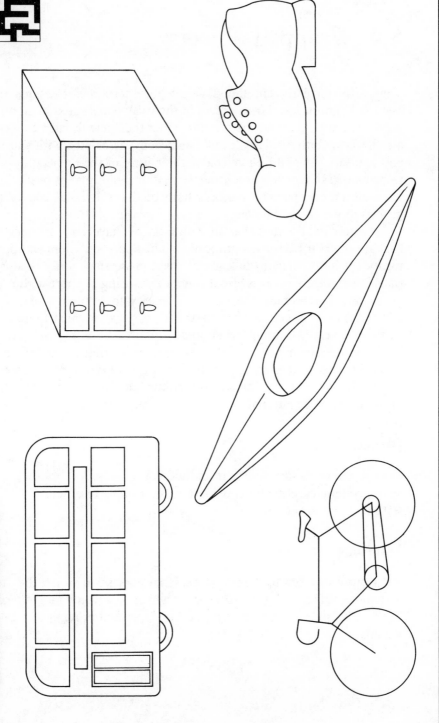

5.4 Wrapped objects

Very often in early childhood we acquire certain possessions that assume a significance far in excess of their value measured in all other ways. These possessions are often toys but they may be such things as a soft warm cloth or blanket that has become associated with warmth and comfort. As children get older the nature of their prized possessions changes, sporting and other recreational equipment or clothing often become important symbols both of the individual and of the groups to which they belong.

This activity assumes that all young people have some possessions that are of great personal significance. The approach offers an opportunity for individuals to talk about these possessions and the stories that lie behind them. It is also a way of enhancing support within the group and heightening the group's capacity for mutual trust. This activity is most effective when used with groups in which there is an existing level of mutual trust and support. Because the activity requires participants to carefully question each other it also enhances basic language and listening skills. The pupils need to move around freely so it is best if the classroom furniture can be moved to the sides of the room or an alternative open space can be found.

Objectives

- to promote self-awareness in individuals
- to promote careful and considerate questioning of others
- to increase group-awareness

Materials

Each pupil is asked to identify a personal possession which they feel says something about them as a person which they would like others to know. The objects are to be wrapped in paper and brought to school. Pencils

Procedure

a Put all the wrapped objects into a large bag or box and mix them up in a way that prevents association with the owners through any feature other than those of the objects themselves.

b Each of the pupils takes an object at random. (Check that no one recognises the object from its wrapping paper.)

c The class unwrap their objects.

d Explain that the purpose is to identify the owner of the object by indirect questioning. The rules governing the questioning are:

- no direct questions connected with ownership, ie 'Is this yours?' is not allowed;
- questions must be of a general nature: 'Are you the kind of person that might wear a badge like this?', 'I know that you are a collector of badges. Is this the kind of badge you might collect?'
- when the questioner is sure that they have identified the owner a direct statement may be used: 'I think that this badge is yours, because . . . '. Such statements should always include a reason.

e When the owner is discovered the object is given back to him and the questioner sits down at the side of the room where others can see him.

It may be necessary to stop this activity before all the objects are returned to their owners. If this happens ask the people with unreturned objects to form a line. Owners to whom objects have not been returned form a second line, facing the first. The object holders are asked to describe the objects to the rest of the class who are invited to help them question the potential owners. If this still fails to match owners to objects, then the owners are invited to come forward and explain the significance of their particular objects.

Prompts for reflection

- What made it difficult for me was . . .
- What I noticed during this exercise was . . .
- I hadn't realised before but . . .
- What I've learned about this group is . . .

Suggestions for follow-up work

1 Invite the class to form groups of four and find out from each other the significance of their chosen objects.
2 Make up a large wall chart listing all the objects brought into the group. Invite the class to form small groups and to try to identify any patterns of similarity that appear within the overall list. Are there individual objects which do not appear in any general pattern? What patterns of similarity and difference are revealed?
3 Make up a large wall chart listing the reasons individuals give for bringing their chosen objects. Invite the class to form small groups and search for patterns of similarity and difference in the stated reasons listed.

5.5 Roots

Young people live their lives as members of many groups. For most the family, neighbours, the local community, membership groups (Scouts, Guides, Youth Club etc), school in general and particular teaching groups feature largely.

In any one class of young people some individuals will have a well-developed knowledge of the life of many other members; some will have partial knowledge about a smaller number of their fellows and a few will have little or no knowledge about the rest of the class. This activity offers an opportunity for all class members to say something about themselves in the context of how they live their life in school, and to hear what others have to say about the same thing. Though the activity is set within the school and local community it lends itself equally well to broader or narrower perspectives (see *Suggestions for follow-up work*).

Objectives

- to reflect on how individuals spend their time, and with whom they spend it
- to offer an opportunity to individuals to speak publicly about themselves

Materials

A packet of self-adhesive labels
A large wall chart or plan showing the school, ideally indicating the feeder primary schools, parks, shopping areas and so on within the school's catchment area

Procedure

a Set the scene by talking about yourself in the context of the chosen chart. This may include a reference to where you live or where you were born, which areas you visit, which roads you travel along coming to work, which shops you use etc. You may also wish to say something about yourself in terms of relationships: the departmental group you work within, your role within the school pastoral system, the group of colleagues to whom you feel allegiance and with whom you spend time. By talking in this way you will set the style and form of presentation. It is an opportunity to give of yourself and as such authenticate this process for others.

b Place a sticker bearing your name at the point on the general plan which you feel best represents your strongest association with the school and the people within it.

c Invite members of the class to take it in turn to repeat the procedure for themselves, describing where they live, which feeder junior/middle school they went to, their chosen route to school and the places where they meet their friends in school and out of school. Finally they say which part of the overall plan they associate with most closely.

d As each pupil finishes, place a sticker with his name on it at the chosen point on the plan.

Prompts for reflection

- I decided to put my sticker where I did because . . .
- The other places I could have put my sticker were . . .
- What surprised me about this activity was . . .
- What I didn't realise was . . .
- During the activity I felt . . .

Suggestions for follow-up work

1 Invite the class to form groups and write down the statements given by individual members. Collect these in and mount a class display. Invite the class to form up into small working groups as a basis for identifying patterns of similarity and difference.

2 Repeat the activity, this time on a broader scale, reflecting national or international patterns. This allows the pupils an opportunity to describe their roots more widely and is particularly suitable for a multicultural group.

3 Narrow the approach to home in on the school as a community, using a layout of the classroom blocks, playground etc. Or focus on the classroom itself, using this as a basis for describing working groups and friendship groups within it. (If the latter approach is used, you should consider carefully the effect it may have on any individuals who are not well integrated into the class.)

5.6 You and me

This activity is designed to enhance the established support of group members. With older pupils or adults this method can be used effectively with individuals who are meeting for the first time to work on a common task, but with younger pupils it should be confined to existing friendship groups.

Objectives

- to promote deeper thought about ourselves and others
- to increase sensitivity and support within the group

Materials

One piece of paper per person
Pencils

Procedure

a Arrange the class in pairs seated as comfortably as possible.
b Invite the pairs to talk for two minutes about anything they like.
c Bring the group to silence and ask them to sit in silence for half a minute and think about the person they are with.
d Each person writes down *one* word which describes their partner without letting partners see what they have written.
e They then fold over the top of the paper.
f Each person now writes down the word they *think* their partner has written about them.
g They fold over the paper again.
h Pairs talk with each other on any subject they like for a further two minutes.
i Bring the pairs to silence and ask each member of a pair to list as many similarities and differences between themselves and their partner as they can.
j Finally invite the members of each pair to share with each other what they have written.

Prompts for reflection

- The other words I nearly used to describe you were . . .
- Secretly I hoped you had described me as . . .
- I hadn't realised before that we both . . .

Suggestions for follow-up work

1 Repeat the same procedure with different pairings.
2 Repeat the same procedure but ask pupils to think about specific tasks or functions eg What word describes your partner as a friend? as a student? as a son/daughter? Link these to patterns of similarity and difference in terms of friendship groups, study routines, school work, family.

5.7 Personal gifts

Many of us develop a capacity to receive criticism as a matter of course, yet we remain ill-at-ease when it comes to receiving positive statements of support. This activity and the next, *Proud circle* are designed to help individuals focus on positive feelings for one another and express these in writing and orally. The activities offer pupils opportunities to understand how others see us and to deal with positive personal support. The activity is most effective with a group that is already working well.

It may be that some pupils receive little personal support from their peers. You should try to anticipate this as far as possible, and it may be best to avoid this activity if you judge that any pupil's self-esteem is likely to be undermined by it.

Objectives

* to help individuals know what positive feelings others have for them
* to encourage individuals to think more deeply about others

Materials

Strips of paper
Pencils
An envelope for each pupil

Procedure

a Hand out the envelopes and ask each person to write his name on the front.
b Pin the envelopes to the notice boards in the classroom, or lay them out on desk tops.
c Hand out the strips of paper; at least enough for each person to write a statement about half the people in the class.
d Invite the class to write positive statements for individuals in the class. Each statement should be on a single strip of paper with the

sender's name and the receiver's name. (10 minutes) Emphasise that the statement should be in the form of a gift, eg 'I give you good luck with your coming music exam.' 'I give you a big smile.' 'I give you the hope that you get the bicycle I know you want.'

Prompts for reflection

• The gift that I like most is . . .
• The gift I most enjoyed giving was . . .
• The gift I would most like to receive but didn't is . . .
• What I liked about this activity was . . .

Suggestions for follow-up work

Follow the same procedure but focus on specific types of gifts, eg study skills, personal attributes . . .

5.8 Proud circle

This activity, like the preceding one, challenges young people to focus on their positive attributes and reflect these in personal pride. It relies to a great extent on each individual's ability to step outside his own identity and see his friends in terms of what they can be proud of.

This is a demanding and powerful way of working with a group, and will require considerable preparation. Indeed, all of the preceding activities and experiences have been leading up to this point. To work best, the activity should be introduced when there is a calm and positive atmosphere in the classroom. An ideal time might be when a group has achieved something they have worked for together, or at the end of a particular period in the life of a group – a theatrical or musical production, the end of a sports season, the conclusion of a school field trip or period of work experience, or the end of the school year.

Allow plenty of time for this activity, as it should not be broken off in mid-sequence.

Objectives

- to think more deeply about each other
- to speak positively about ourselves and each other
- to promote sensitivity and group support

Materials

None

Procedure

a Invite the class to form groups of four or five, preferably where members have experience of working together and/or are friends.

b Join one of the groups to demonstrate to the class how a 'proud circle' round operates. (You should have agreed this with the group beforehand, and run through the procedure with them.) The round consists of statements which begin:
'My name is . . . and I am proud of . . . '

Begin by speaking as yourself:
'My name is Miss Jones and I am proud of the way I organise my lessons.'
Then go on to speak as if you were each of the other members of the group:
'My name is Maureen Brown, and I am proud of my sporting ability; my name is Rita Patel, and I am proud of my friendliness to people; my name is David Hunter and I am proud of my skill at drawing . . . '
c Each member of the group repeats the procedure, speaking first for themselves and then for each of the other group members.
d Since the activity is about personal reflection, it may be most appropriate to debrief with prompts for silent consideration (see below).

Prompts for reflection

- During that activity I felt . . .
- The reasons other people gave for my own pride which surprised me were . . .

Suggestions for follow-up work

1 Repeat the activity with an agreed point of focus. For example where the groups have worked on projects it can be part of the final self assessment procedure to tell each other what contribution or achievement they are proud of personally and what they feel are the contributions and achievements that their group members should be proud of.
2 The same idea can be used but adapted by changing the word proud. For example introducing such words as 'contribute to the group by' allows a focus on roles and actions in the group.

5.9 Role continua and inventory

We all play a variety of roles in the groups to which we belong. To our parents we are son or daughter, to our children, father or mother. In our work we may be 'the boss' while in our leisure time we may come under other people's control.

Young people take roles within their school groups. This activity is designed to make them more aware of how they fulfil roles in relation to each other and that to do so can be a matter of choice.

Objectives

- to provide an opportunity for class members to work as teams
- to reflect on personal performance in a team

Materials

One *Task information sheet* for each pupil
A set of *Group observer checklists* for each group
One *Role continua sheet* for each pupil

Procedure

a Invite the class to divide up into groups of five or six.
b Hand out the *Task information sheets*.
c Ask groups to read the information and check with each other that they understand the task. (5 minutes)
d Give one extra minute for the groups to choose their individual observer.
e Hand out the *Group observer checklists* and allow two minutes for the observers to confirm that they know what their task is and how to do it. The other members of the groups should be using this time to check their understanding of the overall task, particularly the fact that they will be observed and have the observations reported back to them.
f Invite the groups to start their tasks and quickly check that the observers are clear about their task.

g Groups complete their tasks. (15 minutes)
h Groups take turns to present their poems to the whole class.
i Invite the observers to describe to the groups what they have seen.
j Collect from all the observers a list of specific words and phrases about things that members of the group have done eg made suggestions, argued, remained silent, made decisions, wrote out the poem, presented the poem, kept the peace . . . Write these up on a flip chart, blackboard or overhead projector transparency.
k Hand out the blank *Role continua sheets* to all members of the class. Invite them to write the words from the list on the sheet.
l Invite the class to form up into pairs and help each other to identify where they feel they should place themselves on the continua.

Prompts for reflection

Observers
• During the time when everyone was active and I was observing I felt . . .
• The most difficult task for me was . . .
• What I noted about our group as a whole was . . .
Other group members
• The part I enjoyed most was . . .
• For me working in a team is . . .
• The most frustrating part of the activity was . . .
• I hadn't realised before that . . .
• During the activity I learned that . . .

Suggestions for follow-up work

Invite individuals to consider the groups to which they belong – youth clubs, teams, choirs etc and to work out a set of roles that people play in those groups.

Task information sheet

* you are asked to write a poem about the weather.

* the poem is to be presented to the rest of the class.

* the poem should have 3 verses.

* the poem should rhyme.

* the poem should use all of the following words.

rain	shine	blow	ice	sun	gale
nice	hail	fine	drain	fun	snow

* more than one person should be involved in presenting the poem to the group.

* you have 15 minutes to plan and complete the poem and prepare and rehearse your presentation.

Group observers checklist

CHOICES

1 Write the names of your group members in the boxes at the top of the columns.

2 Read the list of words down the left of the sheet. If you are unsure what they mean check with your teacher.

3 Observe the group. Listen to what they say. Watch what they do. If a person does any of the things listed, tick their box, level with the word describing what they did.

gives support	☐	☐	☐	☐	☐
offers ideas	☐	☐	☐	☐	☐
argues	☐	☐	☐	☐	☐
silent	☐	☐	☐	☐	☐
writes	☐	☐	☐	☐	☐
decides	☐	☐	☐	☐	☐
presents poem	☐	☐	☐	☐	☐

Role Continua Sheet

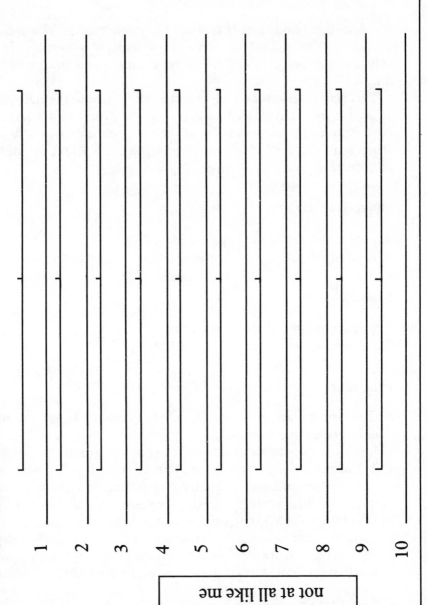

1

2

3

4

5

6

7

8

9

10

not at all like me

5.10 Class family tree

The idea of a family tree is appealing to many people. The notion of tracing back our ancestory gives us a sense of our roots. It also enhances our perception of where we fit into an on-going pattern of life.

This activity takes these ideas and applies them to the class group. It invites the individuals that make up the group to see how they contribute to the corporate life of the class through their individual characteristics, all of which are valued either as a source of similarity or difference.

Objectives

- to give the class a view of itself as a group
- to compare patterns of similarity and difference in a group

Materials

Flip chart or large sheet of newsprint
Thick felt-tip pen

Procedure

a Clear the furniture to the sides of the room, or better still find a large open space to work in.
b Invite the class to stand close together as one group.
c Ask members of the class in turn to state one thing that every one of them has in common. If there are many suggestions, accept all of them and then invite the group to vote on the one they like most. Write the accepted statement at the top of the large sheet of paper.
d Invite the class to invent a simple way of dividing the whole group. On this basis invite the class to form two groups. Write the basis for the division in the form of a question under the intitial statement on the paper.
e Invite the sub-groups to invent a second simple question to further subdivide the groups. Again divide up the groups and write up the agreed question.

f Continue until everyone in the class is in a sub-group of one and a full set of questions has been written up on the large sheet of paper.
g Ask for a volunteer to describe himself using the responses to the questions.
h Hand out small pieces of paper for each person to write down their list of characteristics – according to the questions. Figure 5.b shows a typical series of questions and responses an individual might make.

		Responses
Opening statement	We are all members of class 1BH	member of 1BH
Question 1	Boy or girl?	girl
Question 2	Brown eyes or not?	brown eyes
Question 3	Long hair/short hair?	short hair
Question 4	Only child/brothers and/or sisters?	sisters
Question 5	Musical/not musical	musical
Question 6	Sporting/not sporting	sporting
Question 7	Good at French/not good at French?	not good

Thus in this example the pupil would write: 'I am a brown-eyed, short haired, musical, sporting girl in 1BH who is not good at French and I have sisters.'

Fig. 5.b

i Finally invite the whole class to walk around introducing themselves to each other using their full list of responses.

Prompts for reflection

• The main things I noticed in that activity were . . .
• The person most similar to me was . . . and he/she was . . .
• The person most different to me was . . . and he/she was . . .
• What I now know about this class is . . .

Suggestions for follow-up work

Use the same basic procedure but restrict the pupils to one specific aspect of the life of the class. Possibilities are hobbies and personal interests, performance in different subject areas, travel experience etc.

6 Practically perfect

The title of this chapter is particularly appropriate, since it conveys a view of the state in which, at best, we all hope to find ourselves. The activities focus on personal disability. They seek to emphasise that while differences between the able-bodied and the disabled do exist, they may in total be less than we might suppose. The major difference is probably one which exists between any two people, ie that each sees the world differently. Perhaps the outward manifestation of a disability serves to heighten any apparent differences, but we may reasonably deduce that, whatever the disability, we all share certain ambitions and needs, know joy and sorrow and experience pain.

Although severe disability may restrict activity in certain aspects of a person's life, this is by no means inevitable. For example, in areas such as art, drama, music and sport, the talents of some severely disabled people exceed those of their able-bodied peers. We seek to emphasise the positive attributes of all people and to reinforce the notion of 'sharing abilities', ie that we should share the talents we possess in order to complement each other's actions in the pursuit of happiness, mutual support and understanding.

Misconceptions and myths about the disabled are legion and have done a great deal to create and sustain fears in some young people. Many such fears are based on little or no experience of meeting, living or working with people who have a disability. We believe that it is wrong to see the disabled as some kind of generic group or category, as the nature and extent of disability varies from person to person.

Clearly, it is impossible to write materials which are applicable to every individual, group, class or school, therefore the responsibility for the selection and presentation of appropriate materials must rest with the teacher. Offence may inadvertently be caused if one is not sensitive to the way in which people may view the activities. If any of your pupils have known disabilities you may need to select from, or adapt, the activities in the light of this.

The activities in this chapter centre on disabilities of which the pupils may have first-hand experience within the community, home or school. *My ideal person* seeks to demonstrate that no-one can be or do everything; the able-bodied are no more likely than the disabled to possess the attributes, characteristics and skills of the ideal person.

When a specific disability is mentioned it is likely that particular experiences, images, phrases and words come to mind. In *My word* pupils examine, through a word-association activity, the stereotypes they use. Many prejudices are based upon anxieties, and the section on *Fears* invites pupils to confront and discuss their fears and to consider ways in which they may be allayed or reduced.

There are times when one hears generalised statements about the plight of the disabled in society, so in *Do you agree?* pupils are asked to consider their positive and negative feelings, examine their assumptions and discriminate between statements of fact, opinion and fantasy.

It is difficult to simulate disability; the role play situation is a temporary and reversible state in which a person is unlikely to experience the mental and physical difficulties of a disabled person. However, in *How does it feel?* pupils are given a practical glimpse of what certain aspects of a disability may mean to an individual. The experience of short-term disability, eg a broken leg, may be familiar to some pupils, but long-term incapacity is likely to be unfamiliar.

If the disabled are perceived as being different, *Weekend leisure activities* is likely to encourage young people to consider such views.

The majority of people consider themselves to be able-bodied, and thus the design of local amenities may not always reflect the needs of people with disabilities. In *Facilities* pupils mount an enquiry into the problems faced by people with specific disabilities. The school may be one site worthy of close scrutiny, and in the final section, *Welcome*, groups are asked to consider how they would include a disabled pupil who joins their class, and what specific differences, if any, would be desirable in the induction.

We hope that as a result of these activities, pupils will consider to what extent the differences between the able-bodied and the disabled are real or illusory. They may go on to further investigations, with the support of the teacher, which will give them first-hand experience and provide answers to questions *they* wish to ask.

6.1 My ideal person

The image-makers of the media seek to persuade young people that to be an acceptable or desirable person one has to behave and dress in a particular way. The projection of the ideal person is part of the powerful imagery used by promoters to market a wide range of products. Living in a consumer world, young people are bombarded by 'the ideal' and may become intolerant of those products or people who do not match the image.

Even our closest associates and friends do not possess all of the attributes and characteristics we would expect to find in the ideal person, but nevertheless we still value their company and support.

In this activity, pupils consider the notion of the 'ideal person' and draw comparisons with their friends. Although the able-bodied may appear, from their outward appearance, to be 'ideal', they cannot be or do everything any more than can a person who one may describe as 'disabled'.

Objectives

- to show that few people possess all the attributes and qualities which we value in our 'ideal person'
- to examine the characteristics of people we admire but have not met

Materials

Pencils
Plain writing paper
A copy of the *My ideal person* worksheet for each pupil
Overhead projector/blackboard

Procedure

a Write the following incomplete sentence on the blackboard or an overhead projector transparency:
   'My ideal person is someone who is . . . '
b Distribute a blank piece of paper to each pupil and ask them to write down words or phrases which complete the sentence. (3–4 minutes)

c Invite pupils to say what they have written. List the responses under the written sentence until the available area is covered with contributions.

d Give each pupil a copy of the *My ideal person* sheet (p 149). Ask the pupils to select their 'top ten' attributes from the listed items and write them in the left-hand column.

e Invite each pupil to think about five people with whom he is friendly, within and/or outside his family. (Emphasise that at no stage should the writer reveal the identity of his chosen subjects). Each pupil labels the five chosen people A, B, C, D and E. Then, for each one, he puts a tick in the appropriate box on the sheet, as shown in Figure 6.a. (10–12 minutes)

My ideal person is someone who is . . .

	A	B	C	D	E
Brave	√		√		√
Funny	√	√	√	√	√
Generous		√	√	√	√
Good-looking	√			√	√
Happy	√	√		√	√
Honest		√	√	√	√
Humble	√	√	√		√
Loyal	√	√	√	√	√
Reliable	√	√	√	√	√
Rich		√	√	√	

Fig. 6.a   Example of completed proforma

f Remind pupils that the identity of A, B, C, D and E should not be revealed. Divide the class into random groups of four or five, by using the alphabetical order of the first letter of a pupil's first name, for example Group 1 would contain Anne, Ahmed, Barbara and Bernie, Group 2 Belinda, Balbia, Carl, Catherine . . . Group 8 Wendy, William, Winston, Zak . . .

g Group members take turns to select the letter which most closely matches their view of the ideal person and then read out and elaborates upon the attribute. The other group members listen and note any points about the 'ideal person' which they wish to talk about later. After each member has made his uninterrupted contribution, everyone is free to share observations with the group. (15 minutes)

h Ask the group to use the words recorded at the start of the session to describe one or more famous people who may be considered 'ideal'. (This final task in the form of a discussion provides an opportunity for consideration of the things one admires in people with whom there has never been face-to-face contact.)

Prompts for reflection

- The most important thing I have learnt during this session is . . .
- Being perfect means . . .
- My ideal adult is someone who . . .

Suggestions for follow-up work

1 Ask pupils to examine catalogues, magazine and newspaper advertisements and to write down the qualities portrayed by the people featured in them.

2 Invite pupils to undertake research into the ways men and women are portrayed on goods and displays in shops, or in television commercials.

My ideal person is someone who is . . .

CHOICES

	A	B	C	D	E
1					
2					
3					
4					
5					
6					
7					
8					
9					
10					

1986   David Settle/Charles Wise   Basil Blackwell

6.2 My word

There are occasions when, although not directly involved in a conversation, we may overhear a word or phrase which sparks off thoughts about other associated words, phrases and situations. In this activity the class uses a 'word association' technique in order to investigate members' *feelings* about particular disabilities. This approach is designed to accommodate the many and varied viewpoints that are likely to be found in any one class.

The activity requires each pupil to describe, in private, his reactions to a named disability. His anonymously completed proforma is then used by another individual in the group as a basis for discussion.

Objective

● to explore positive and negative feelings about the disabled

Materials

A copy of the *My word* sheet (page 153) for each pupil
Pencils

Procedure

a Give each pupil a copy of the *My word* sheet and a pencil. (Ask pupils *not* to write their names on the paper.)
b Describe what is meant by 'word association'. Explain that when a word is mentioned, the pupil should write down other words which come to mind, without too much deliberation.

  Point out that for the word 'food' two words have already been written on the right-hand side of the sheet. Pupils may write two more words associated with 'food' in the spaces below. Check that all pupils understand the procedure before continuing with the activity.
c Invite the class to suggest a disability, of a temporary or a permanent nature, that a young person may experience eg blindness,

deafness, broken pelvis, no speech, poor movement. Ask pupils to write this on the left-hand side of the form, under the word 'Food.'

d Ask the class: 'When you hear the word '. . . ', what other words come into your mind? Write up to four words in the boxes alongside the word '. . .'.

e Repeat the procedure until the chart has been completed. Only one disability word should be inserted in the left hand box at a time, followed by the related words of association. (15 minutes) Pupils exchange papers at least four times during the process so that they cannot be linked with a particular paper (handwriting will be the only means of identification).

f Ask the class to form groups of four to six. Using the proforma they now hold, each member places a tick by words which may be described as 'warm' or 'positive', a cross by words which are 'cool' or 'negative' and a circle around words which do not fall into either category. (3–4 minutes)

g The group takes one disability word (as written in the left hand column) at a time and discusses the related words on each sheet. Which are 'warm'; 'cool'; 'neither'? If members suggest that words placed in one category are misplaced, these should be reallocated.

h Invite pupils to express their opinions relating to what they have found out about feelings towards those with disabilities.

Prompts for reflection

● The best word I heard was . . .
● The worst word I heard was . . .
● I think a disabled person may have been pleased to hear the word '. . .'.
● I think a disabled person may have been upset to hear the word '. . .'.

Suggestions for follow-up work

1 Invite pupils to collect photographs and articles from magazines and newspapers which show disabled people participating in the life of their local community.

2 Ask groups to investigate local social and sports clubs which welcome the involvement of both disabled and able-bodied young people.

3 Invite the class to consider ways in which it may mount an investigation based upon one of the following issues:
- ways in which people minimise their disability in the home;
- ways in which the disabled in the local community assist and support each other;
- the policy of local firms towards employing the disabled.

The class may wish to identify a specific disability for study.

My Word

Example: Food	Happy	Hungry
1		
2		
3		
4		

1986   David Settle/Charles Wise   Basil Blackwell

6.3 Fears

The feelings of able-bodied people towards the disabled may take many forms, for example anger, detachment or hostility. The roots of such feelings are not always apparent to the person concerned or to those who observe the resultant behaviour.

In this activity pupils create their own statements relating to fears which they or other people may have about the disabled. If there is a tendency for some class members to express exaggerated negative views in order to impress their peers, you should explain that the activity is concerned with handling fears rather than attempting to shock. Some pupils may not be able to describe what they fear (if anything) and discussion with you may help them produce a written statement. The final stage of the activity is devoted to the consideration of how we may allay or resolve our fears.

This activity does not attempt to persuade young people that their fears are irrational or unwarranted, but rather to provide a forum in which they may consider the consequences of their behaviour and feelings for themselves and for others, and which may enable them to reassess their stance.

Objectives

- to explore the feelings of fear that pupils have about the disabled
- to consider how more positive feelings towards the disabled can be induced in young people

Materials

Blank cards (two per pupil)
A hat or shoe box for each group of eight
Pencils

Procedure

a Divide the class into groups of six to eight. Provide each group with a hat or shoe box, and each pupil with a pencil and two blank cards. The group sits in a circle, with the hat or box in the centre.

b Invite each pupil to write two sentences (one on each card) which express his or other people's fears about the disabled. If necessary, use Figure 6.b to show what is required:

I would be frightened to meet a disabled person in the dark.	I would not like someone with a damaged hand to touch me.

Fig. 6.b

Each sentence should be expressed in the first person. Try not to intervene unless it is obvious that pupils cannot find anything to write. (5 minutes)

c Pupils place the completed cards in the group's hat or box.

d Each group nominates someone to start the next phase of the lesson. Alternatively, select the person whose surname is closest to, or begins with, A. One by one pupils draw a card from the hat and read out the statement. As if he were the author of the statement, each pupil elaborates upon his fears. If a pupil draws his own card, he should complete the activity without indicating this.

e The other pupils follow this procedure until all the cards have been drawn and described. Only the pupil with the card should talk. When the speaker has finished he places the card face downwards alongside the hat. (8–10 minutes)

f You could repeat the exercise in order to build up pupils' confidence.

Prompts for reflection

- I think my feelings about the disabled are due to . . .
- My fears are based upon . . .
- Some television programmes show the disabled as . . .
- The disabled can teach me something about . . .

Suggestions for follow-up work

Ask each pupil to use one of the following media to describe the fears which a group of young people of their age might have about the disabled: collage; drama; music; painting; poetry; prose.

6.4 Do you agree?

In the previous exercise, we focused upon negative feelings. In this activity, we present 20 contentious statements which require pupils to consider a broad spectrum of fact and opinion. The statements used represent some of the beliefs which one might encounter in society, from popular misconceptions and myths through to statements of fact. They present a challenge to our deep-seated prejudices as well as provoking consideration of the value we place on human beings. Pupils are invited to discuss the accuracy and appropriateness of assumptions and generalised statements.

The aim of the activity is to help pupils appreciate that although a statement may receive support from the majority of people in a group, this does not necessarily confer on it the status of a fact. The distinction between 'fact' and 'opinion' may not always be apparent, therefore debate and research may be necessary. Within this activity, moments of uncertainty may provide triggers for further investigation.

If any of the statements are likely to cause embarrassment or offence, they should be removed and replaced by more suitable ones.

Objectives

• to investigate pupil opinion relating to the nature of disability
• to stimulate interest in action research relating to the disabled

Materials

A set of the *20 statements* for each group
Three cards for each group with the headings *Agree*, *Disagree* and *Don't know*

Procedure

a Divide the class into an *even* number of small groups. Each group should contain three to five members, gathered around a table or work surface.

b Give each group a set of the *20 statements*, presented as separate cards, together with three cards labelled *Agree, Disagree* and *Don't know*. Explain that these three cards are to be placed at the top of three columns. Group members should then negotiate the distribution of the other cards under these headings. (There may be a tendency for pupils to respond quickly and place a large number of cards in the *Don't know* column in the early stages. Encourage the group to engage in discussion, and only to place cards in this column if doubt remains, or as a last resort if an agreed response cannot be achieved.) (7–10 minutes)

c Each group spends a few minutes preparing a justification for the distribution of the cards, prior to joining another group.

d Groups pair up, leaving their cards in place.

e One group acts as 'host' and explains their display of cards; the 'visitor' group examines the arrangement, and may seek further clarification and explanation.

f The roles of the two groups are reversed, ie the 'visitor' becomes the 'host' group and the procedure is repeated. (10 minutes)

g The groups return to their original work bases. Remind pupils that the decision to place a card in a particular column does not indicate that the statement is necessarily 'true' or 'false'. Ask each group to select one or more statements which members wish to investigate more fully. The basis of the enquiry is likely to take the form of either an opinion survey or the collation of factual information to support or discredit the statement.

Prompts for reflection

- The most difficult statement to reach agreement on was . . .
- The statement which made me feel most angry was . . .
- The statement which made me feel happiest was . . .
- Being 'disabled' means . . .
- I am keen to find out what disabled people feel about . . .

Suggestions for follow-up work

Invite the class members to construct alternative sentences which could be included in a card sort exercise.

20 Statements

CHOICES

Disabled people have many talents	Everyone should feel sorry for disabled people
A person who is blind is more disabled than someone who is deaf	Disabled people are not all the same
People who are disabled are often grumpy	Every disabled person of any age should receive £100 a week from the state
Able-bodied people deserve the best paid jobs	Many people dislike sitting near disabled people
Disabled people do not understand what is happening to them	Every able-bodied person should spend at least three hours a week with a disabled person

CHOICES

As people grow old they become disabled	All people who are confined to a wheelchair should have a free TV licence
Everyone in the world has a disability	Disabled people often get poorly paid jobs
Able-bodied people can learn a great deal from the disabled	The disabled are treated like second class citizens
Able-bodied and disabled people should help each other to enjoy life	Some employers are keen to employ the disabled
Some of the world's most talented people may be considered to be 'disabled'	The term 'disabled' means being ill

6.5 How does it feel?

It is clearly impossible to accurately simulate the conditions surrounding the experience of being 'disabled'. However, able-bodied pupils may gain increased understanding if there is a change in their own physical state which inhibits their normal functioning. It must be emphasised, however, that the experience of a short-term disability such as a broken leg is likely to differ considerably from that of a permanent, life-long situation such as spina bifida.

In this activity a range of physical disabilities may be examined, or you may wish to focus upon one specific situation. The virtue of having a single focus is that teacher and class members can explore the inferences and consequences of the activity in depth. It is important to allow plenty of time for reflection and discussion at the end of this activity. Giving pupils the opportunity to describe their feelings will greatly enhance the learning process.

Because the simulated 'disability' is a temporary state, the capacity to draw conclusions as to how one might feel if it were 'for real', is limited, since the accompanying possible mental trauma cannot be readily assessed. However, for all its limitations, the activity may provide insights into the otherwise hidden world of disability and it may stimulate pupils' interest in working with the disabled within the community and other schools.

Objectives

• to provide pupils with a simulated experience of a disability

Materials

One *Disability card* for each group
Enough of the following to support the work of the whole class when divided into groups of three:
Blindfolds
Pencils
Travel brochures
Writing paper
Wheelchairs (if these are not available, one pupil could sit on a chair

with two others to carry him – acting as 'wheels'. The chair can move forwards, backwards and diagonally, but the height *cannot* be adjusted)

Procedure

a Ask the class to divide into groups of three. Give each group one of the *Disability* cards, with details of a disability.
b Pupils label themselves **A, B,** and **C. A** is the subject on the card, **B** their partner and **C** an observer.
c All pupils read the card. **C** checks that **A** and **B** are clear about their respective roles. If necessary, **C** offers clarification.
d It is the responsibility of **C** to set the activity in motion and to ensure that both of the other partners fulfil the terms of the contract as described on the card.
e **A** and **B** take on their roles and act out the situation on the card. (10–15 minutes)
f The parties de-role and discuss their feelings about the experience. At this point you may wish to use one or some of the *Prompts for reflection* below to stimulate discussion.
g Where time permits the roles may be changed, using the same or a different card.

Prompts for reflection

- I realised what it was like to be disabled when . . .
- The experience was unrealistic because . . .
- My major difficulty was . . .
- When watching the role play, I felt . . .
- My feelings about the disabled are . . .

Suggestions for follow-up work

1 Invite the class to devise other activities which simulate the experience of being disabled.
2 Ask pupils to find out about local organisations for the disabled. If there is a PHAB (Physically Handicapped and Able Bodied) Club in the community, pupils may wish to join a social gathering. Or pupils may wish to make links with a local special school to discuss the possibilities of starting a club there.

Disability cards

Blindness
Wear a blindfold. Walk along the corridors with a sighted partner. Ask him or her to guide you where necessary.

Paralysis below the waist
In a wheelchair, travel to the library to collect a book from the top shelf of the highest bookcase. A partner may accompany you to ensure your safety, but may offer no further help.

Broken writing arm
Write a letter with your 'wrong' hand. In the letter, you should explain the accident to a partner. He or she will be nearby to receive your letter.

Loss of speech
With an able-bodied partner you plan a 10 day summer holiday with the help of a brochure. You have no speech.

Deafness
Your partner wishes to tell you a piece of good news. He or she cannot talk to you so you have to watch his or her actions. What is he or she trying to tell you?

No arms
Write your name on a piece of paper. A partner will give you writing materials, but cannot help in any other way.

6.6 Week-end leisure activities

This activity is designed to illustrate how we often make decisions on the basis of limited information.

Four groups are each provided with the profile of a girl. They all have identical information apart from one statement. Working independently, each group extends the profile in order to give a more complete picture of 'Miss Smith', as perceived through the way she uses her leisure time.

It is impossible to anticipate what differences between the imaginary girls will emerge. However, it is likely that there will be a number of issues related to the pupils' perceptions of being able-bodied and disabled that will offer rich learning potential.

You may have to curtail the activity due to the duration of the lesson. However, try to leave three or four minutes for a de-briefing session.

Objectives

- to use existing experience and knowledge to build up a picture of the leisure activities undertaken by young people with specific disabilities
- to stimulate discussion on the limitations, or limiting effect, of one's preconceptions about the disabled

Materials

One set of *Miss Smith* profiles
Sheets of newsprint
Four thick felt-tip pens
Masking tape or blu-tak
Four blank cards for each group (16 cards)
Pencils

Procedure

a Divide the class into four groups, as far as possible of equal numbers. Groups should be spaced so that members cannot easily overhear the discussion of another group.

b Give each group *one* of the four *Miss Smith* profiles, together with a sheet of newsprint and a felt-tip pen. Ask groups to write the full name of Miss Smith (as per their profile) on the top of the sheet, in block capitals. No other information from the profile should be written or attached to the newsprint. Explain that there should be no discussion between members of different groups. Groups should not be told that there is a difference in each profile.

c A nominated group member draws a line down the middle of the paper and heads the column on the left *Likely* and the right-hand colum *Unlikely*. The purpose of the task is to list, using single words and short phrases, the leisure activities in which group members believe Miss Smith may or may not participate during the week-ends. Extra sheets of newsprint should be available. (12–15 minutes)

d Still without any discussion between groups, display the pieces of newsprint on the wall.

e Give each group four blank cards and a pencil and ask them to record one of the names of Miss Smith on each card (see Figure 6.c)

Fig. 6.c

f The groups look at the wall displays and decide which one line of information was different on each of the profiles. (Explain that all the other information was common to all the profiles.) At this stage there should still be no discussion between different groups. As soon as the group is confident that it has identified the different line, a scribe writes down on each card what the line says on the respective profiles.

g When a group has written its four cards, the scribe brings them to you. Check the cards for accuracy. If the four cards are correct, finish the activity for the whole class and tell everyone the answer. If one or more cards are incorrect, inform the group. The scribe returns to the group and they amend their response. At no time should you indicate which card(s) contain incorrect information.

h Use the *Prompts for reflection* below, or pupil observations relating to the value of the activity, to conclude the session.

Prompts for reflection

- Today I learnt that . . .
- The value of the lesson was that . . .
- I need to know more about . . .
- I was surprised that . . .

Suggestions for follow-up work

1 Individually or in groups, invite the class to investigate the weekend leisure activities popular among young people who are considered to be 'disabled'. Encourage pupils to identify examples where able-bodied and disabled enjoy the same activities, in order to develop the notion of 'sharing abilities'.
2 Invite pupils to mount a project on the Paraplegic Games.

Miss Smith

CHOICES

Sally Smith

Is 13 years old
Lives in a semi-
detached house
Has two older brothers
Very happy person
Is fit
Both parents drive the
family car
She has many friends

Rachel Smith

Is 13 years old
Lives in a semi-
detached house
Has two older brothers
Very happy person
Is blind
Both parents drive the
family car
She has many friends

Claire Smith

Is 13 years old
Lives in a semi-
detached house
Has two older brothers
Very happy person
Is deaf
Both parents drive the
family car
She has many friends

Michelle Smith

Is 13 years old
Lives in a semi-
detached house
Has two older brothers
Very happy person
Is confined to a
wheelchair
Both parents drive the
family car
She has many friends

6.7 Facilities

This activity should extend over a series of lessons; it offers numerous points for departure and development. Although the preparation and debriefing session may take place during the school's working day, the pupils will need to devote additional time to the tasks.

To enable pupils to gain greater insight into the plight of the disabled, this long-term enquiry focuses upon the design and provision of amenities and facilities within the local community. Pupils are expected to frame their own questions, develop observation schedules and plan how they wish to present their findings. Their primary responsibility is to their respective groups rather than to the whole class. Each group decides upon the nature and scope of its work; more than one group may focus upon the same disability but they should be encouraged to work independently.

Objectives

- to visit a local communal facility and investigate its actual and potential hazards for the disabled
- to increase awareness of the difficulties experienced by the disabled in using local facilities

Materials

Felt-tip pen and large sheet of newsprint for each small group
Plain writing paper
Pencils

Procedure

a Ask pupils to form friendship groups. Display the list of facilities (Figure 6d). Each group selects one of the facilities to visit in order to identify the actual and potential hazards *for a person confined to a wheelchair*.

Airport	Leisure centre
Bank	Mosque
Bingo Hall	Museum
Boutique	Post Office
Chapel	Public conveniences
Church	Restaurant
Cinema	School
Citizens Advice Bureau	Shop
Council offices	Stadium
Day centre	Supermarket
Hairdresser	Synagogue
Laundrette	Youth Club
Theatre	

Fig. 6.d

(Explain that the disabled person has a power-assisted chair and has full use of his arms and hands.)

b Issue each group with a sheet of newsprint and a felt-tip pen. Group members use the brainstorming technique to compile a list of the hazards they might expect to find within their chosen facility. (Up to 8 minutes)

c From the list, the group selects the same number of features as there are members, ie a group of six has six features. For example, a group which plans to mount its enquiry in a supermarket may have identified

  1 Access to and from the store
  2 Movement around the store
  3 Height of fixtures
  4 Weighing facilities for fruit and vegetables
  5 Check-out area
  6 Access to fridges

(10–15 minutes)

d The members negotiate a suitable division of labour so that each pupil takes responsibility for investigating *one* of the features 'through the eyes' of the disabled person.

e Each member may wish to sub-divide the feature so that his observations are sharply focused during the visit (see Figure 6e)

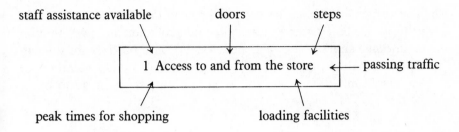

staff assistance available   doors   steps

1 Access to and from the store ◄── passing traffic

peak times for shopping   loading facilities

Fig. 6.e

(Up to this point the tasks will probably have taken 40 minutes.)

f Members of the group may need to contact a manager or key personnel in order to gain access and/or permission to conduct the enquiry. It is for the group to decide who will liaise with the outside agency and how this should be done. You may be able to offer school facilities – eg telephone, headed notepaper, typewriter – to support the pupils' work.

g The development of an observation schedule by pupils may assist their enquiry (see Figure 6f). If group members adopt a common format, they may find that their report-back is more structured and less time-consuming than if they were ploughing through reams of rough notes.

Facility: Supermarket   Date of visit: 11.11.86
Feature: Access to and from the store

Issues for attention	Observation
doors	
loading facilities	
passing traffic	
peak times shopping	
staff assistance available	
steps	

Fig. 6.f Observation schedule

h The responsibilities of each member need to be agreed within the group. Deadline dates for the collection, collation and presentation of findings should be established. Groups also need to consider in detail how the information is to be presented to other members of the class, and the nature and scope of any report made to other bodies.

Prompts for reflection

• Planning an enquiry requires . . .
• The benefits of working on a collective task include . . .
• Being confined to a wheelchair must be . . .
• Being able-bodied means . . .
• I value my own physical state because . . .

Suggestions for follow-up work

1 It would be interesting for the pupils to check their observations with disabled people. The opportunity for an accompanied visit during the enquiry may add an extra dimension to the learning process.
2 Invite pupils to investigate the possibilities of sharing their observations with other groups of pupils in the school; organisations for the disabled; local councillors; the key personnel of the facility.

6.8 Welcome

Although this activity centres upon the arrival of a new class member who is disabled, it has a more general application in terms of the induction of any pupil to an established grouping.

One of the major issues which is likely to emerge is that of whether or not special provision should be made for a disabled person. Being treated in the same way as able-bodied people may do a great deal to enhance the self-esteem of a disabled person. However, there are circumstances when, due to the severity of the disability, the helping nature of the welcome and sustained support will be greatly appreciated.

If there are disabled pupils in the class you need to think carefully about how they might perceive this particular focus. Is it condescending? Is it undermining the dignity and self-respect of the individual? Whatever the circumstances, when *any* pupil joins a new grouping, due care and attention should be paid to the welcome that is extended.

Objectives

* to identify the critical events that may be experienced by a new pupil during his or her first day in school
* to explore ways of supporting a new pupil who joins the class

Materials

Eight *Information cards* (page 174)
Eight overhead projector pens (preferably water-soluble)
Eight overhead transparencies
Overhead projector
Plain writing paper for each group
Pencils

Procedure

a Divide the class into eight groups.
b Place the eight information cards (each containing brief details

about an imaginary pupil) face downwards on a central table. Invite a member of each group to select one card for his group.

c Explain to each group that the person described on the card will be joining this class on Monday morning: 'S/he is joining us because s/he was unhappy in her/his previous day school'. Explain that although the whole class is likely to help the new pupil settle in to school, the identified group has agreed to take specific responsibility for the newcomer's welfare.

d Each group discusses how it will ensure that the first day will be a pleasurable experience for the new pupil. (5 minutes)

e Each group selects a scribe, who is given an overhead projector pen and transparency. The group spends 10 minutes identifying critical events during the first day when members' support may be necessary (see Figure 6g).

---

1 Pupil arrives on the school premises
2 In the playground before school starts
3 Going to registration
4 Introduction to tutor/form teacher
5 Payment of monies
6 Collection of timetable, meal tickets, homework book and school diary
7 Journey to first lesson
8 Introduction to teacher
9 Playtime/break
10 Lunch time
11 Arrangements for dining
12 ....

Fig. 6.g

f Using their knowledge of the school, pupils devise their own schedule.

g The group decides how the scribe should record the agreed procedure on the overhead transparency (15 minutes). It is a group collective responsibility to provide the scribe with information. Explain that the scribes should use single words or short phrases to describe each event or phase, so that the presentation to the class is clear and readily understandable.

h Each scribe displays and presents the group's deliberations. A one minute presentation should be sufficient time for each contribution. Invite the rest of the class to comment at the end of each group's display.

Prompts for reflection

- When any pupil joins this group we will . . .
- I think the most important event during a person's first day at school is . . .
- As a new pupil in this school, I felt . . .
- We do not need to make special arrangements for a new pupil because . . .
- I think a new pupil would be most upset if . . .

Suggestions for follow-up work

1 Ask groups to discuss in detail how they would help the new pupil to minimise the difficulties encountered at each of the critical events identified in their respective schedules.
2 Invite pupils to recall their first few days in their present school and reflect on the success of the induction process.

Information cards

Mandy is deaf

Errol is blind

Hanifa has two artificial arms

Rob is confined to a wheelchair

Rajesh suffers from chronic asthma

Kim is partially-sighted

Carl has recently lost the use of his writing hand

Nicki wears calipers on both legs and uses a walking stick

7 Food for thought

We are fast becoming a more food conscious nation, though some would argue that we are still not sufficiently aware of the part that diet plays in everyone's life.

There is ample evidence to demonstrate the connection between diet and physical and mental state. Among the most startling illustrations of this link are the known effect of food additives on the level of hyperactivity in some children, and the relationship between fibre content of diet and the incidence of bowel cancer.

It has also become clear that publicity campaigns directed at improving dietary composition *do* have an effect. The impact of publicity can be illustrated by the halving of the incidence of heart disease in the United States, which can be directly attributed to the government campaign to reduce the intake of high cholesterol products such as butter, cheese and other milk products in favour of an increase in fresh fruit and vegetable consumption as part of a greater intake of high fibre foods. Of course the part played by exercise in the success of the American scheme cannot be underestimated but the overall winners are those members of society who respond positively to their own awareness of basic choices in life concerning diet and exercise.

This fundamental principle lies behind this entire book, and in particular this chapter. Namely, the responsibility of teachers to raise young people's awareness of the serious choices ahead of them in their lives, and of the part they must play in taking direct positive action to make their own considered decisions.

In planning such work with pupils we need to consider the confusing picture created by conflicting publicity. Individuals can hardly be blamed for being confused about what makes up a healthy diet. The enormous sums of money spent advertising a vast range of foods continue to have a major impact on our eating habits. Add to this the growing number of high street suppliers of pre-packed convenience foods – presented as fun meals for happy eaters – and the battle to improve our eating habits is clearly by no means won.

Nevertheless there is evidence of growing commercial interest in the sales of healthier foods. A number of the large supermarket chains have introduced items which they market specifically on a ticket of healthy eating. Some supermarkets take this a stage further by making available well-presented leaflets on healthy eating. It is ironic that commercial enterprise is now demonstrating a more holistic approach to dietary education when so many schools and colleges, probably unthinkingly, demonstrate conflicting practice between the theory of classroom experience and the reality of what is offered over the counter of the tuck shop and school canteen.

The general aims of this chapter are to raise pupils' consciousness of the daily dietary decisions in their lives; to increase pupils' knowledge of what makes up a healthy diet within the context of overall healthy living; and finally to increase pupils' appreciation of the variations of dietary content in different ethnic groups together with the part this variation can play in providing a more interesting, exciting and healthily balanced diet.

All the activities in this chapter can be used independently. However they are much more effective when used in a developmental sequence. One possible sequence is: *'Diet – facts I know', Eater's diary/ Group eaters' diary', 'Recipe exchange', 'My friend as food'* and *'Fantasy feast'*. These five activities focus on what the pupils already know about diet as a starting point for further study. They also have a strong personal/interpersonal emphasis. A second possible developmental sequence that focuses more on factual information to be discovered through investigatory methods might be *'Food sales pattern action research', 'Health foods investigation', 'Looking for Es'* and *'Hidden persuaders'*.

7.1 Eater's diary/Group eaters' diary

For most young people, and for that matter most adults, the intake of food over a period of days probably does not reflect a conscious decision to ensure a balanced intake of dietary components. We tend either to be totally regimented in a pattern of eating controlled by established habits or completely haphazard in our choice of food. In this activity it is not suggested that young people should become slaves to a pre-planned pattern of eating but rather that they should be made more aware of the effects of their particular personal diet through studying what they eat over a period of five days. On the basis of this enquiry their dietery intake can then be analysed to see if any major imbalances can be detected. These imbalances can themselves become the basis of a further enquiry over a longer period of time.

The first entry in the diary will correspond to whatever day of the week the class meets. For this reason the 'day of the week' and 'data' boxes are left blank on the *Eater's diary*. The booklet also includes space to record Saturday's and Sunday's intake. This will allow an interesting comparison to be made between weekday and weekend intakes of food, and patterns of eating. The dietary component boxes on each sheet allow a crude check to be made on the intake of carbohydrates, fats, proteins, minerals, vitamins and fibre provided by the meals.

Objectives

- to build up a personal record of eating
- to promote interest in patterns of healthy eating

Materials

An *Eater's diary booklet* for each pupil
A copy of the *Dietary components checksheet* for each pupil

Procedure

a Give each pupil a copy of the *Eater's diary* booklet and the *Dietary components checksheet*.

b Each pupil fills in the cover and the details of his current day's food intake.

c Now invite the pupils to work in pairs to help each other analyse the dietary components of their food using the *Dietary components checksheet*. For each component identified a single tick is placed in the appropriate box at the side of the sheet. The number of ticks for each box reflects that day's pattern of intake.

d Invite the pupils to enter into a contract with each other to complete the entries for each day of the week until the class meets again. (It may be helpful to enlist the support of the form's pastoral tutor for this activity so that pupils can be given the few minutes each day that are necessary to complete one page of the booklet.)

e When the class meet again check to see how many have completed their booklets. Allow time for those who have incomplete booklets to add whatever information they can recall.

f Working in pairs, the class complete and check over each other's dietary component analysis and fill in the boxes accordingly.

g Pupils then add up the ticks in each components box over the whole week and write the number of ticks in the appropriate space on the cover.

h Organise the class into groups of four to compare each other's overall patterns of dietary intake. The *Prompts for reflection* below may help stimulate discussion.

Prompts for reflection

- What I hadn't noticed about my eating habits is . . .
- What I hadn't realised about this group is . . .
- The thing I would most like to change about my eating habits is . . .

Suggestions for follow-up work

1 Invite members of the class to produce histograms of their dietary intake to show the patterns of components.

2 Ask pupils to produce a class histogram of dietary intake. (Pupils might ask teachers in the Maths department for other ideas about graphic representation of data.)

3 Pupils could compare weekday with weekend patterns of intake and/or compare the intake of members of different ethnic groups in the class.

4 Pupils could conduct research into 'healthy' diets, and compare the individual or class eaters' diary with a recommended balanced dietary intake. (Teachers in the Home Economics or Biology departments should be able to help with this.)

Dietary components checksheet

CHOICES

Figures marked ★ from 'Multipurpose food products' Bihar, India. All others from HMSO Manual of Nutrition	Protein g.	Fat g.	Carbohydrate g.	Calcium mg.	Iron mg.	Vitamin A µg.	Vitamin D µg.	Vitamin B mg.	Vitamin C mg.
Milk dried whole	26.6	27.7	37.6	813	0.7	246	0.30	↝	11
Milk skimmed powder★	38.0	0.1	51.0	–	–	–	–	–	–
Yoghurt natural	3.6	2.6	5.2	140	0.1	22	0.02	↝	0
Cheese cheddar	25.4	34.5	0	810	0.6	420	0.35	↝	0
Buttermilk★ (liquid)	0.8	1.1	0.5		–	–	–	–	–
Bacon average	11.0	48.0	0	10	1.0	0	0	↝	0
Beef average	14.8	28.2	0	10	4.0	0	0	↝	0
Mutton★	18.5	13.3	–	–	1.5	–	–	–	–
Chicken raw	20.8	6.7	0	11		0	0	↝	0
Kidney average	16.9	4.2	0	14	13.4	300	0	↝	12
Liver average raw	16.5	8.1	0	8	13.9	6000	0.75	↝	30
Pork average	12.0	40	0	10	1.0	0	0	↝	0
White fish	16.0	0.5	0	25	1.0	0	0	↝	0
Fish fingers	13.4	6.8	20.7	50	1.4	0	0	↝	0
Sardines canned	20.4	22.6	0	409	4.0	30	7.50	↝	0
Eggs	11.9	12.3	0	56	2.5	300	1.50	↝	0
Butter	0.5	82.5	0	15	0.2	995	1.25	≈0	0
Margarine	0.2	85.3	0	4	0.3	900	8.00	≈0	0
Milk chocolate	8.7	37.6	54.5	246	1.7	6.6	0	↝	0
Honey	0.4	0	76.4	5	0.4	0	0	0	0
Jam	0.5	0	69.2	18	1.2	2	0	0	10
Ice cream	4.1	11.3	19.8	137	0.3	1	0	↝	1
Baked beans	6.0	0.4	17.3	62	2.1	50	0	↝	3
Broad beans	7.2	0.5	9.5	30	1.1	22	0	↝	30

Dietary components checksheet — continued

Figures marked ★ from 'Multipurpose food products' Bihar, India. All others from HMSO Manual of Nutrition	Protein g.	Fat g.	Carbo-hydrate g.	Calcium mg.	Iron mg.	Vitamin A µg.	Vitamin D µg.	Vitamin B mg.	Vitamin C mg.
Runner beans	1.1	0	2.9	33	0.7	50	0	✓	20
Cabbage raw	1.5	0	5.8	65	1.0	50	0	✓	60
Lentils dry	23.8	0	53.2	39	7.6	6	0	✓	0
Ground nut★	26.7	40.1	20.3	–	–	–	–	–	–
Cashew nut★	21.2	46.9	22.3	–	–	–	–	–	–
Almond★	18.6	54.1	19.6	–	–	–	–	–	–
Soyabean★	43.2	19.5	20.9	–	–	–	–	–	–
Dried peas★	19.7	1.1	56.6	–	–	–	–	–	–
Chick peas★	22.5	5.2	58.9	–	–	–	–	–	–
Millet★	11.6	5.0	67.1	–	–	–	–	–	–
Maize dry★	11.1	3.6	66.2	–	–	–	–	–	–
Wheat flour★	12.1	1.7	72.2	–	–	–	–	–	–
Carrots	0.7	0	5.4	48	0.6	2000	0	✓	6
Onions	0.9	0	5.2	31	0.3	0	0	✓	10
Peppers green	1.2	0.5	3.7	9	0.7	42	0	✓	128
Potato raw	2.0	0	18.0	8	0.7	0	0	✓	30
Spinach	2.7	0	2.8	70	3.2	1000	0	✓	60
Apple	0.3	0	12.0	4	0.3	5	0	✓	5
Banana	1.1	0	19.2	7	0.4	33	0	✓	10
Guava★	1.5	0.2	14.5	–	–	–	–	–	–
Mango★	0.6	0.1	11.8	–	–	–	–	–	–
Pawpaw★	0.5	0.1	9.5	–	–	–	–	✓	–
Orange	0.8	0	8.5	41	0.3	8	0	–	50

© 1986   David Settle/Charles Wise   Basil Blackwell

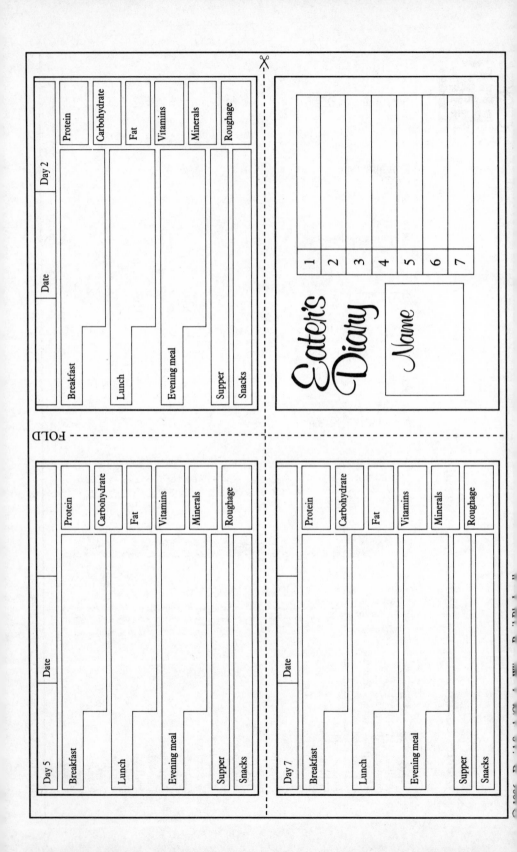

Day 2   Date

Breakfast

Protein

Carbohydrate

Lunch

Fat

Evening meal

Vitamins

Minerals

Supper

Roughage

Snacks

FOLD

Eater's Diary

Name

1
2
3
4
5
6
7

Day 5   Date

Breakfast

Protein

Carbohydrate

Lunch

Fat

Evening meal

Vitamins

Minerals

Supper

Roughage

Snacks

Day 7   Date

Breakfast

Protein

Carbohydrate

Lunch

Fat

Evening meal

Vitamins

Minerals

Supper

Roughage

Snacks

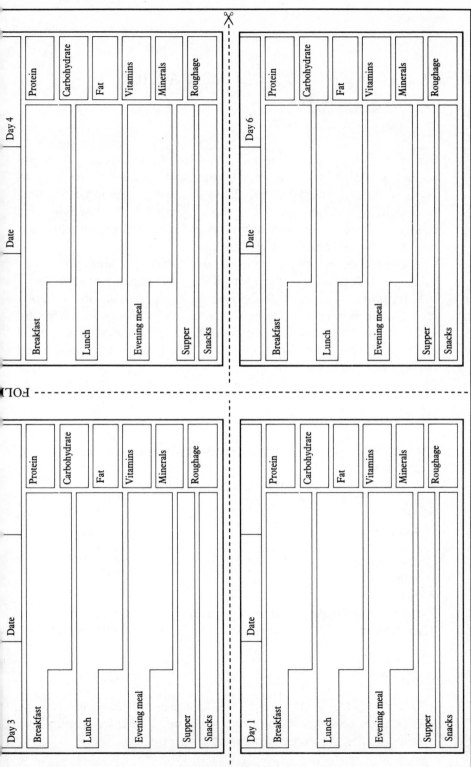

7.2 Food sales pattern action research

This activity offers a way for pupils to collect information on the topic of diet as reflected in the local patterns of food sales. As well as providing useful information it allows the group to undertake a common task, so building their team working capacity. The activity also reinforces the idea that learning takes place outside school when the resources available are used effectively.

The procedure requires considerable forward planning. It also needs good cooperation on the part of the shopkeepers and others who will form the subject of the enquiry. In some cases the school's circumstances or a particular policy decision regarding pupils working out of school may make this activity difficult. As an alternative, pupils could carry out a similar (though less effective) survey using their parents and neighbours.

Objectives

- to produce, by cooperation, an agenda for an investigation outside school
- to collect factual information by direct investigation

Materials

Paper
Pencils
A map of the area
Large sheets of sugar paper or newsprint
Standard letter to the manager/owner (to be copied for use by groups)

Procedure

a Display a large-scale map of the area around the school, or the collections of shops in the school catchment area. Invite pupils to help identify each shop, restaurant etc on the map.

b Explain that the purpose of the activity is for the class to carry out an investigation of the patterns of food sales as part of the overall work on dietary intake.

c Pairs of pupils choose one or more shops/restaurants to investigate as their own part in the enquiry. Write pupils' names on the map against particular locations to show the overall distribution.

d Explain the need for some form of preliminary communication to seek the support of the shopkeepers and to agree a time for the enquiry to be carried out – in school-time, after school, at the weekend . . . Provide the class with a letter which pupils can individually sign and then deliver to the particular shopkeeper(s) they hope to visit. (Ideally the class should produce its own letter, but you may not think this advisable in terms of the extra time required or the ability of the pupils involved.)

e In small groups, pupils decide the kind of information to be collected from shopkeepers. Each group prepares three questions.

f Collect the questions, one at a time, from the groups, until an overall set emerges. Check that these questions deal with such issues as customers' preferences for fresh or for prepackaged foods; or for health foods such as high-fibre bread, low carbohydrate products and non-additive foods such as pure fruit juice.

g Prepare a final checklist of questions to be used by the group. (Ideally this should be typed up and photocopied.) The checklist should be ready for the start of the lesson when the class will carry out the enquiry, or soon after the shopkeepers have replied, if the enquiry is to be done in the pupils' own time.

h When all the pupils have conducted their investigations, invite the pairs to write up their findings on large sheets of sugar paper or newsprint. Display these sheets around the classroom in the form of a gallery. Other members of the class read the displays and search for patterns in the findings.

i Using the original questions, collate the information gathered by the whole class. Invite individuals to produce a report to be fed back to the shopkeepers they visited.

Prompts for reflection

- The reactions I got from the shopkeepers were . . .
- Just before carrying out the investigation I felt . . .
- After the investigation I felt . . .
- What surprised me most was . . .

Suggestions for follow-up work

1 Invite pupils to carry out a similar investigation of health food sales from specialist shops and compare the pattern of sales with those of other shops.
2 Pupils could compare the pattern of food sales for supermarkets with those of small specialist shops.
3 Suggest that pupils write to food manufacturers requesting information on how they market products.
4 Pupils could invite a manager, buyer or dietician to visit the class, to complement their action research.

7.3 Health foods investigation

This activity involves pupils in two forms of enquiry into the nature of health foods. So much is written today about healthy eating and the advantages of certain types of diet and methods of growing food that it is important for young people to be sufficiently well-informed to make up their own minds about this issue. This activity uses an action research approach by a representative group to carry out a preliminary enquiry as a preparation for the whole class to receive a number of 'experts' as visitors to their group. (For an outline of the approach to receiving a visitor, see Chapter 2, page 28.)

Pupils will need access to a local health food shop or restaurant for this activity. Some supermarkets now have health food sections or a health foods policy, so the manager of such a supermarket could also be approached. You will also need a number of 'experts' on health foods who would be willing to visit the school.

Objectives

- to investigate what is meant by 'health foods'
- to create a situation where a small group carries out a piece of research on behalf of the whole class, and reports back
- for the whole group/class to take responsibility for receiving a visitor

Materials

Agreed set of *Statement cards*

Procedure

a Invite the class to form groups of four.
b Hand out a set of *Statement cards* to each group.
c Ask the group to arrange the cards into sets, on the basis of their current knowledge of what can be described as health foods.
d Each group displays its arrangement of cards. Class members walk around the room comparing the arrangements.

e You may need to help pupils discern any patterns which arise from the way in which groups have arranged the statement cards.

f Ask pupils to return to their original groups of four and create a single statement describing what they understand by the term 'health foods'.

g Tell the class that you are going to invite a number of visitors who are 'experts' on the subject of health foods, to give them first-hand information. Explain the need for a small group to carry out a preliminary enquiry as part of the preparation for visitors. (Arrangements for this should be carried out as described in the previous activity *Food sales patterns.*)

h Identify a group of not more than four to carry out an enquiry with a health food shopkeeper or restaurant owner. (If more opportunities exist this can be broadened to include more people. However, part of the purpose is to create a situation where a small group undertakes a piece of work on behalf of the whole class.)

i Invite the class to agree on the form of questions to be used in the enquiry, based upon the outcomes of the first part of the enquiry.

j Arrange for the group to visit the shop or restaurant.

k Provide an opportunity in the next lesson for the sub-group to report back their findings to the whole class. On the basis of this information, invite the group to agree on a set of questions to put to an 'expert' visitor.

l Organise the class into sub-groups according to the number of visitors available. Prepare these groups using the approach described in Chapter 2, pages 19–20.

m Debrief the activity using the prompts below.

Prompts for reflection

• The things I now know about health foods are . . .
• What I hadn't realised about health foods is . . .
• What surprised me most about health foods is . . .
• My attitude towards health foods is . . .

Suggestions for follow-up work

No specific suggestions for extension work are included in view of the complex nature of the activity. However, the procedures adopted lend themselves to a whole variety of different situations as well as contributing to the group's effectiveness in team work.

Set of statement cards

health foods are high in protein	health foods contain little animal fat	health foods have a high salt content	health foods contain no additives
health foods are irradiated to delay their decay	health foods are grown using lots of pesticides	health foods have a high sugar content	health foods have all the mineral salts removed
health foods are grown using lots of fertilizer	health foods are mainly imported from abroad	health foods are organically grown	health foods allow you to lose weight easily
health foods give you more energy	health foods increase resistance to disease	health foods prolong active life	health foods are always fresh

7.4 Looking for Es

One of the 'changes' that could have been included in Chapter 4 of this book is the appearance of E numbers on food packaging over the last few years. Although additives have been used to preserve foods for thousands of years it is only relatively recently that this practice has extended to include artificial flavouring, flavour-enhancing chemicals and artificial colouring as well as antioxidants. As the E numbers suggest there are a lot of them (see Table on page 193). In the last few years they have started to attract attention because of the correlation between the use of certain additives in fruit drinks and the incidence of hyperactivity in young children.

The purpose of this activity is to increase young people's awareness of the additives in their foods, especially 'trash' foods, and to enable them to make an informed choice between artificially colourful and tasty foods with additives and more natural foods.

Objectives

- to investigate the use of additives in foods
- to investigate the patterns of use of additives in a variety of foods

Materials

Food packets/labels etc (as many as possible)
A copy of the *Food checker chart* and *Table of E numbers* for each pupil.

Procedure

a Some weeks before the activity, ask the class to collect and bring in food packets, labels etc in order to build up a large stockpile. Ask pupils to cut out the sections describing the food contents, additives etc.
b Explain that for each food pupils should enter the name in the left-hand column of the table. Alongside it, they should write each of the E numbers in a separate column, putting the same E numbers in the same column to show the frequency with which they are used.
c Invite the class to produce a display chart of foods and additives.

Prompts for reflection

- What I have learned about the use of food additives is . . .
- What I feel about the use of food additives is . . .

Suggestions for follow-up work

1 Invite pupils to identify foods which contain no additives and write to the manufacturers explaining the purpose of this study and requesting further information on their policy regarding the use of additives.
2 Collect brief and readable articles on food additives from food magazines etc.
3 Groups of pupils could get together to produce a quiz/facts finder on additives to give to other groups in the class, or other classes.

CHOICES

Food checker chart

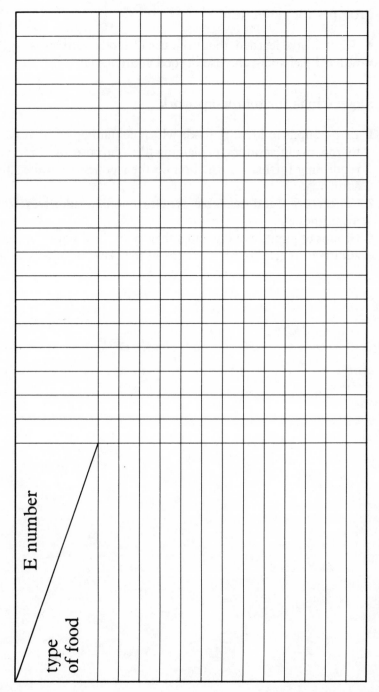

type
of food

E number

Table of E numbers

CHOICES

CHOICES

Table of E numbers – continued

Anti-oxidants E300–E321

E300 Ascorbic acid (vitamin C)
E301 Sodium Ascorbate
E302 Calcium Ascorbate
E304 Ascorbyl Palmitate
E306–309 Tocopherols (vitamin E)
E310 Propyl Gallate
E311 Actyl Gallate
E312 Dodecyl Gallate
E320 Butylated Hydroxyanisole
E321 Butylated Hydroxytoluene

Emulsifiers/stabilizers E322–E494

E322 Lecithins
E325–327 Lactates
E330 Citric Acid
E331–330 Citrates
E33 Tartaric Acid
E335–337 Tartrates
E338 Orthophosphoric Acid
E339–341 Orthophosphates
E400 Alginic Acid
E401–405 Alginates
E406 Agar
E407 Carrageenan
E410–416 Gums
E420 Sorbitol ⎫ sweeteners
E421 Mannitol ⎭
E422 Glycerol – solvent
E430–431 Stearates
E432–436 Polysorbates
E440 Pectin/Pectates
E442 Ammonium Phosphatides
E450 Phosphates
E460–466 Cellulose Compounds
E470–483 Fatty Acid Salts

E numbers are EEC codes used as standards by UK and EEC manufacturers. Other substances are currently under consideration by the EEC for an 'E' prefix.

For further details see 'E for Additives' by Maurice Hanssen, Thorson Publishers.
ISBN 0-7225-1150-7

7.5 Recipe exchange

We all need to be able to prepare food for eating. But although many of us are capable of performing the mechanical tasks, we are less able to take account of the dietary value of what we are preparing. This activity is intended to support the notion that everyone should be able to prepare food and that as part of this process they should take account of the dietary components they are providing. The activity has the added bonus of starting from where the pupils are in dietary knowledge.

Objectives

- to use each other as a learning resource
- to increase awareness of how to ensure a balanced diet

Materials

Pencils
Paper
A copy of the *Recipe exchange* sheet for each pupil

Procedure

a Ask the class to work as individuals for the first part of the session.
b Invite pupils to think of a meal they like to cook for themselves.
c Pupils list the ingredients of this meal on the *Recipe exchange* sheet and then describe the method of preparation and cooking in the next section. In the third section, they list the known dietary components of the food, and finally they say whether they think this is a healthy food, explaining why/why not. (For reference, see the *Dietary components* checksheet on pages 180–181.)
d Invite pupils to organise themselves in pairs and question each other about the meals they have described, in order to find out as much detail as possible.
e Remind the class that they should be listening carefully to what their partner is saying, since they will shortly represent their partner in a group of four.

f Combine pairs to make groups of four.

g Invite each person to speak *as if they were their partner* about the meal their partner has described.

Prompts for reflection

• I chose my particular meal because . . .

• What I learned about my partner was . . .

Suggestions for follow-up work

1 Invite pupils to form groups of four to share their described meals and work out the order of healthy eating they would place them in.

2 Working in pairs, pupils could take it in turns to analyse their partner's described meal in terms of its dietary components, ie minerals, proteins, vitamins etc.

Recipe Exchange

Name
Ingredients
Preparation and cooking

Protein	Dietary components and health quality of food
Fat	
Carbohydrate	
Calcium	
Iron	
Vitamin A	
Vitamin B	
Vitamin C	
Vitamin D	

7.6 My friend as food

One of the ways we demonstrate knowledge of our close friends is through describing their preferences and dislikes, especially with food. Simple examples might be knowing if a friend has sugar in their coffee or prefers tea to coffee.

This activity uses this natural interest and desire to know about others as a basis for finding out more detailed information about diet. This knowledge, in turn, becomes the focus of a deeper insight into healthy eating.

Objective

● to learn about a friend's eating habits

Materials

Paper and pencil
Large display sheet

Procedure

a Arrange the class in groups of four.
b In these groups pupils make up a list of questions they could use to obtain precise information about a friend's eating habits eg Do you have sugar on your cornflakes? When you get up do you drink tea, coffee, milk or water? Do you prefer brown sauce or tomato sauce?
c Asking each group of four to contribute one question at a time compile a single set of questions on the display sheet for the whole class to use. Now invite the class to form up into friendship pairs and see how many of the questions they can answer on behalf of each other.
d Invite the friendship pairs to check their answers with what each person would really choose.

Prompts for reflection

- I found that I know . . . about my friend's eating habits
- The parts that I knew most about were . . .
- What my friend did not know about me was . . .
- What surprised us both was . . .

Suggestions for follow-up work

1 Using the same structure of questions invite pupils to check their knowledge of parent's, brother's, sister's eating habits.
2 Take the individual sheets of information prepared by each pupil in response to the displayed questions and put them into a large box. With the whole class seated in a circle take out one sheet at a time and read out facts one by one until someone in the group can identify who the owner of the sheet is.

7.7 Diet – facts I know

For a class starting out on a study of food and diet it is important to establish their existing knowledge. This particular activity provides an effective way of quickly checking on the group's common knowledge as a basis for future work – it is also good fun! Because the activity is open-ended it is important to set a time limit; about 15 minutes should be sufficient. If before time is up only a small minority have been unable to identify the owners of the questions, introduce a new approach by asking these individuals to read out each question publicly to see if anyone can answer it before the originator owns up and answers it for the group.

Objectives

• to establish how much the group already knows about diet and good eating habits

Materials

Two pieces of A5 paper per person

Procedure

a Start the group off with all pupils working independently.
b Ask each person to think of two questions on diet, good eating or food, to which they think only they know the answer. Each pupil then writes the questions down on separate pieces of paper. (Point out that the questions must be factual, and not relate to personalised knowledge 'What is my Uncle Bert's favourite breakfast?' is not acceptable!)
c Pupils fold up both pieces of paper separately, then the group quickly exchanges the papers as many times as possible in 20 seconds.
d Explain that the object is to find the person who knows the answers to the two questions. (This may take a considerable time, but it is worth it in order to establish with the group their view of what the

topic is about.) It is likely that some of the questions will not be matched against their owners, since another member of the group will have been able to answer them.

e Finally, in order to establish a view of the class's collective knowledge, display all of the questions on large pieces of paper around the classroom.

Prompts for reflection

• What was unusual about this exercise was . . .
• What I liked about this exercise was . . .

Suggestions for follow-up work

1 Take the questions from the class and obtain an agreement on acceptable/unacceptable answers for each question. Invite pupils to put the acceptable ones into categories as a basis for dealing with the work on this topic.

2 Keep the questions and see how many more pupils can answer at the end of this unit on diet and healthy eating.

7.8 Hidden persuaders

Young people spend considerable sums of money on food, confectionary and sweets. Their total spending represents a major proportion of the revenue of many manufacturers and retailers. They are therefore an important part of the market that the advertisers aim to attract. Perhaps the clearest indicators of this are the specialised advertisements that appear on commercial television around the hours of children's broadcasts.

Competition between food manufacturers is very keen and the part played by advertising is crucial both for maintaining existing sales and in breaking into the market with new products. In more recent years it has also become necessary for food manufactuers to use advertising to counter propaganda against their products. Campaigns such as those mounted by the Meat and Egg Marketing Boards are not necessarily there for the good of our health; they are direct attempts to launch a counter-attack in a war of information.

One aspect of this huge upsurge in advertising has been its growing acceptance as an art form. Put quite simply, the quality of the advertisement is more important than the quality of what is advertised until the buyers actually try the product for themselves. A good advertisement can't sell a poor product but it can help a product of equal quality do better than the others in a competitive market. As a consequence there has been a huge upsurge in advertising until we are now surrounded by advertisements. Hoardings and the sides of buses and vans are covered in advertisements. Newspapers and magazines are financed largely through advertising, and the commercial radio and television channels rely entirely on advertising revenue. The danger is that many of us have become so accustomed to this that its influence on our lives is subconscious.

The main purpose of this activity is to raise the consciousness of young people about the purpose and effects of advertising by the food industry.

Objectives

- to investigate the marketing and promotions techniques food manufacturers use to sell their products
- to use the same techniques to create advertisements for health foods

Materials

Widest possible range of advertising materials from magazines, shops and supermarkets – if possible, video recordings of television commercials
Sugar paper
Drawing pins
Felt-tip pens

Procedure

a Number clearly each individual piece of advertising material.
b Distribute this at random around the room or lay it out on the floor in the middle of the room.
c Divide the class into groups of three or four.
d Invite the groups to view all of the advertisements.
e Explain the purpose of the investigation – groups are to search for common patterns of advertising techniques noting the numbers of related advertisements in a particular type of pattern. (10 minutes)
f Invite each group in turn to describe one pattern they have identified and the reasons for their choice.
g Build up a whole class set of these agreed patterns and aim for a consensus view of the techniques being used.
h Invite the groups to collect together advertisements related by common techniques of advertising and mount these on pieces of sugar paper or display boards.
i Through brainstorming in the whole group compile a list of single-word captions to describe the individual collections of advertisements. Write the words alongside the advertisements. (If recorded television commercials are available, invite the class to view them looking for similarities and differences when these are compared with the printed materials.)
j Organise a whole group brainstorm on the approaches used in food marketing, based upon all the available information. Write up the 'rules' and vote on the priority order that advertisers seem to use.

Prompts for reflection

• The things I have learned about food advertising are . . .
• My feelings about food advertising are . . .
• The effects of food advertising on me are . . .
• What I liked most about this activity was . . .

Suggestions for follow-up work

1 *Shopping centre visit* Shopping precincts or large shopping centres provide an excellent environment in which to investigate food advertising. They provide a secure environment for young pupils to work outside school (with adult supervision). They also provide a ready-made resource of people for an action research enquiry. Often such places are used by companies for sales campaigns; this provides an extra opportunity to ask the sales people how they approach their task, at the same time allowing an investigation of the effects such campaigns have on the people they try to influence.

2 *Advertising agencies* As a class exercise pupils could write to a number of food advertising agencies to find out how they carry out their market research and how they make use of their findings. You could find out if one or more will send representatives to the group.

3 *Advertising campaign for school meals* In consultation with the school meals service, the supervisory staff, dieticians and canteen staff within the school invite pupils to mount an advertising campaign. Brainstorm the positive parts of the service and design posters to make use of these facts. Pupils could focus on selling the idea of healthy school meals to other pupils as a basis for an investigation into their eating habits at school.

4 *Health food shops* Check to see if the proprietors of local health food shops are willing to allow visits from schoolchildren. Pupils could also invite the shop owners and managers to the groups as part of an investigation of why people buy health foods.

7.9 Fantasy feast

Young people change their patterns of eating quite often. An eight-year-old's craving for fish fingers may be entirely superseded by hamburgers six months later. But even as adults we may still retain patterns of eating that reflect particular preferences rooted in our childhood.

The idea of this activity is to focus on the foods which pupils like best and to examine the problems that these preferences can bring if they lead to little variation in diet. The issue of variation will be brought out either by the overall variety of preferences displayed by the class or through a clear lack of variety, which can also be used as a learning point.

Objectives

- to allow individuals to express their personal preferences in food
- to analyse the dietary components of each person's fantasy feast

Materials

A class set of *Fantasy feast* sheets
A class set of the *Dietary components checksheet* (see pages 180–181)
Eight sheets of sugar paper, cut into the shape of large serving plates

Procedure

a Invite the class to work in pairs.
b Use the following prompts to promote conversations in pairs:
   - 'Think back to the last time you really enjoyed a meal or snack that you were eating. Find out from your partner about a similar memory.'
   - 'Find out from your partner if the food they described is their favourite food today. If not, what is their favourite food?'
   Remember to be mobile and to use the pupils' stories.
c Hand out the *Fantasy feast* charts and ask the pupils to think of their dream meal. Each partner describes their dream meal and the

other writes it down, listing the individual components in the left-hand column of the chart.

d Hand out the *Dietary components checksheets*. Ask the pupils to work together in their pairs to analyse their dream meals in terms of the dietary components they would contain. Pupils put ticks in the boxes headed *Protein, Carbohydrate* and *Fat*, and list the vitamins and mineral salts in the remaining two columns.

e Hand out small pieces of paper so that each pupil has sufficient pieces on which to write each item of food in their dream meal.

f Lay out the sugar paper 'platters' on a number of desk tops or benches. Label each one Meats, Fish, Poultry, Cheeses, Vegetables, Fruits, Sweets, Drinks. Pupils place the individual foods which made up their dream meals on the separate platters.

g Invite the class to look at the collection of foods from their dream meals that now make up their Fantasy feast.

Prompts for reflection

- The patterns I notice in the Fantasy Feast are . . .
- The changes that would be needed to make the Fantasy Feast a Healthy Feast would be . . .
- The problems with my own dream meal were . . .
- The changes I would need to make to my dream meal to make it a healthy meal would be . . .
- What I liked about this activity was . . .

Suggestions for follow-up work

1 *Historical feasts* Invite the class to research historical feasts using sources such as the *Guinness Book of Records*, local history books etc. Pupils could write to local large hotels asking them for past menus they have designed for banquets. Then ask groups to analyse the information provided using the dietary component charts.

2 *Feasts from other places* With a multicultural class invite groups to design feasts made up of ethnic foods. Follow this up with each group telling the whole class about their individual feasts.

Fantasy Feast

Name _____

Foods	Protein	Carbohydrate	Fat	Vitamins	Minerals	Roughage
1						
2						
3						
4						
5						
6						
7						
8						
9						
10						

CHOICES

8 Resisting social pressures

The purpose of these activities is to help the teacher to make public forces existing within the class that affect the personal choices and decision making of its members. By their organisation, schools require pupils to function in groups. In primary schools these groups are usually fixed for long periods of time; perhaps for the whole school life of each pupil. In secondary schools there is more variation but often tutor groups remain fixed for up to five years and these may be the basis of most teaching groups for at least three years. Whatever the organisational pattern, all pupils are exposed to a complex web of pupil/pupil and pupil/teacher interactions. The effects of these interactions and the form of their expression vary both from group to group and between individuals within groups. For the purpose of this chapter, we will look at six aspects which affect most individuals.

1 Expectations of others

Where groups have a well established history, individuals within them are often held in a straitjacket of other people's expectations, based largely upon memories of past performance. These expectations cover both behaviour and personal performance and can create roles for individuals from which they find it difficult to escape.

2 Roles

Sometimes roles are associated with tasks agreed in public by the group. There are jobs to be done in class and offering these to the group for members to accept is a way of sharing responsibility and experience. But behind these roles are many more which may neither be agreed nor considered by the individual or the group. Nevertheless the roles exist and individuals fulfil them, thus satisfying the expectations of others – which increasingly become their own expectations.

Teachers will be familiar with the class clown, the person who disrupts the group by his comments and behaviour. This role is often well rehearsed; in a working day it may be carried from class to class and operated to a lesser or greater degree according to the varying constraints of teacher control. Where this is the case the individual may acquire such a high order of prominence, even amongst teachers, that they too begin to contribute to the expectations by drawing attention to the role. Other roles may be less public – the peace-keeper, the distractor, the organiser, the source of new ideas, the silent member, but these and many others can be seen to operate in classrooms within the unspoken guidelines of group control.

3 Normative control

Where rules exist it is difficult for the individual to operate outside their control. School rules regarding dress and punctuality are two examples. Though individuals will test the rules by breaking them they will through their actions not only be at odds with their teachers but also with those of their peers who, by their conformity, uphold the rules. In the same way there are other rules, set by the peer group but seldom publicly expressed, which affect individuals. The most obvious and frequently encountered is that of reduced academic performance, where the able pupil, knowing the effects of public acclaim, purposefully underachieves in order to remain closer to the norm within the group. A further expression of this control can be seen in the frequency of offered responses in a class question-and-answer session. Though the bright pupil may be in a position to deal with all of the questions, he may learn that it is better not to be quite so capable or enthusiastic.

4 Friendship and support

Friendship groups in school and college are for many the most significant source of lasting personal support. We need only reflect on our own experience to see where these friends fit into our overall pattern of friendship. For many adults school friends remain significant throughout life. However the teacher needs to be aware of a major point of potential concern; although friendship groups offer personal support they can also be a source of major constraint if they require their members to function within a limited pattern of performance. Under such circumstances there is little support for the individual who may have the capacity and intention to operate outside the expected pattern of friendship group performance. An example might be the case of the girl or boy in a single-sex friendship group within a mixed class who has both the ability and intention to study a subject outside the expected norm of the group. The gender distribution patterns of pupils opting for such subjects as physics, typewriting, home economics and craft, design and technology are illustrative of this point.

5 Assertiveness/aggression

When individuals come into conflict with their groups, especially their friendship groups, it is important that they find a means of expressing their point of view in such a way that they can pursue their personal interests without losing support from their peers. In a sense this may be crudely expressed as 'learning to say no without putting other people down'. Assertiveness can easily slide into aggression and thereby become destructive. It is important, therefore, to give young people opportunities to explore their ability to deal with group pressure in an assertive non-aggressive way within a supportive group where the outcomes are not important.

6 Can't/won't

Where an individual is constrained by his participation in a group there is a tendency for him to express his limitations in terms of 'I can't do this or that'. When this becomes a major issue it is often helpful to challenge the individual to say the same statement, this time replacing *can't* with *won't*.

The activities in this chapter are designed to take the above points into account. Some can be used as single activities but all of them benefit from being combined into a developmental sequence. Out of the first six activities, the *Yes, No game* and the *Yes, Yes, Yes, No game; Group encounters* and *Close encounters*; and *Get out of that* and *Role swopper* all make natural pairs. They also form a sequence of increasing intensity of interaction and experience. *Reds and blues* fits in with the previous sequence by emphasising the potential strength of group pressure. *Story boards* is intended to build on what hopefully has been a growing awareness in pupils that they are all exposed to a variety of pressures within their daily lives.

8.1 Yes, No Game

This is a simple and fun activity that nevertheless rapidly establishes the idea of pressure in a one-to-one situation. It allows individuals to work closely with a partner while remaining totally enclosed within the overall activity of the whole group. Though the procedure suggests that partners are exchanged only once it is worthwhile repeating the process, giving the pupils a number of experiences with a wider range of partners.

The activity is likely to be noisy since many pupils will take this opportunity to shout! A further rule worth adding at a later stage is to require people to whisper in order to see the different effect this has, or even to work in total silence using only non-verbal communication.

Objectives

- to introduce the idea of coping with pressure
- to compare verbal and non-verbal means of communication

Materials

None

Procedure

a Invite the class to form two equal sized groups.
b Ask the groups to line up opposite each other across the room.
c Bring the lines together to form opposing pairs.
d Decide which line is **A** and which is **B**.
e **A** can only use the word *yes*, **B** can only say *no*.
f **A** and **B** pairs are invited to hold a 30-second conversation using only their single words.
g After 30 seconds **A** and **B** are asked to exchange roles and repeat the conversations.
h Bring the group to silence and ask everyone to think about the differences in saying *yes* or *no*. Are there any differences? Which is the most difficult to handle?

i Move one line on by four places taking four people to the other end of their own line. Ask pairs to repeat the exercise.
j Invite pupils to add rules such as whispering or silence in order to emphasise the part played by non-verbal communication.

Prompts for reflection

- For me it was easier to say . . .
- I found it most difficult when I was working with . . . because . . .
- The differences I noticed between the two people were . . .
- When we had to whisper I . . .
- When we couldn't speak at all I . . .

Suggestions for follow-up work

1 Suggest pupils vary the actual words to include phrases – 'Yes you will/No I won't.'
2 Invite pupils to produce their own versions of the opposing phrases and let everyone try these phrases.
3 Allow flexibility of spoken response on one side but total inflexibility on the other 'Oh Yes you will do it'/'No'; 'Yes you will because I can make you'/'No'. Then ask pupils to try reversing these in order to see the relative power of 'Yes' and 'No' in these situations.
4 Following any of the variations in this activity invite the pairs to tell each other of particular situations they have experienced in which they found themselves having to repeatedly say yes or no. Collect these situations from the pairs and use them as an agenda for small group discussions (combine pairs to make fours).

8.2 Yes, Yes, Yes, No game

In the previous activity, saying Yes or No in a one-to-one situation is dependent as much on the existing relationships of the participants as it is on the particular words yes or no. This second activity introduces a variable that is often closer to reality, namely, one person trying to cope with a group response.

As with the previous activity the game may be quite noisy and this should be taken into account when choosing where to work with the pupils.

Objectives

• to experience the effect of pressure from a group on an individual
• to experience being a member of a group pressurising an individual

Materials

None

Procedure

a Invite the class to divide up into groups of three or four.
b Explain that only the words *yes* and *no* will be used in a group conversation.
c Invite pupils to decide who will be the individual first.
d The individual in each group chooses whether he will say *yes* or *no*.
e Groups to hold a 30-second conversation using only Yes or No.
f Ask pupils to reverse roles so that the individual now uses the other word for a further 30 seconds.
g Allow one minute for the group members to tell each other what it felt like to them.
h Repeat the procedure until everyone has had an opportunity to be the individual.

Prompts for reflection

- For me it was most difficult when . . .
- During that activity I felt . . .
- What I have learned from that is . . .
- If that happened to me for real I would . . .

Suggestions for follow-up work

(See previous suggestions for Yes, No game.)

8.3 Group encounters

As with individuals so groups also have a variety of ways of expressing their moods and feelings. The expression of a particular feeling and the behaviour associated with it in a group often has its cause outside the group. For example, the cancellation of a planned class outing would almost certainly result in group depression or anger, whereas the cancellation of lessons for an afternoon might produce an expression of joy. Under either circumstance the group reaction might well be clear but it should not be assumed that it applies to all members. There may well have been an individual for whom the cancellation of the outing was a blessing.

This activity provides an opportunity to explore group expression of feelings and behaviour and to allow individuals to experience these from a position of being excluded.

Objectives

- to allow individuals to experience pressure exerted on them by a group
- to allow individuals to experience a variety of personal interpretations of a single attitude or behaviour
- to allow individuals to reflect on the impact of other people's actions on their own actions in a group

Materials

An open space – hall, gym, outdoors
A set of *Situation prompt cards*

Procedure

a Invite the class to move into or create an open space.
b Pupils move around the room, greeting each other by name as they meet. (30 seconds)
c Pupils repeat activity using only unspoken greetings. (30 seconds)

d Invite the class to repeat the activity once again, this time using only facial expressions to demonstrate the following feelings: happiness, anger, hate.

e Invite the class to form groups of four and use the following prompts for rounds of personal comments:
- While we were doing that I felt . . .
- The part I found most difficult was . . .
- The bit I liked best was . . .

f Ask the class to reassemble, then invite them to organise themselves into five roughly equal sized groups.

g Allocate letters **A** to **E** to the members of these groups.

h Ask the members of **A** to leave the room.

i Read out one of the situation prompt cards to **B, C, D** and **E**. Ask them to agree on a non-verbal way of reacting to it as a whole group.

j Invite the members of **A** back into the room and ask them to spread themselves through the whole group. Now invite the members of **B, C, D** and **E** to react in the agreed way. (30 seconds)

k Stop the activity and invite the members of **A** to describe what they have experienced and to say what kind of situation they think might have caused that reaction.

l Repeat for groups **B, C, D** and **E** using different situation prompt cards.

Prompts for reflection

- When I had been out of the room I felt . . .
- When the group reacted in the way it did . . .
- What I have learned about the group is . . .
- What I have learned about myself is . . .

Suggestions for follow-up work

1 Ask pupils to devise different prompts for the activity, eg Greet me as if I owed you money; as if you owed me money; as if I had an infectious disease; as if I frightened you.

2 Arrange half of the class into pairs – the rest to stay as individuals. Repeat the activities and debrief the effects of being alone or in a pair.

Situation prompt cards

CHOICES

1

You have all been threatened with detention for something that you did not do. You are suddenly told that this has been a mistake. How do you react as a group?

2

You have been planning to present a play for all the parents in the school. Rehearsals have gone quite well but at the last minute your teacher is taken ill. How do you feel?

3

The school badminton team has had a patchy season and struggled to win games but as the weeks go by they improve. They need to win the last match to come top of the league. They lose it. How do you feel?

4

It's a week away from Christmas and preparations for the end of year dance and party are complete. On the day of the party the school toilets are vandalised and the dance is cancelled. How do you react?

8.4 Close encounters

At some stage in our lives we all experience feelings of being out of step with our group; a lack of understanding of what is going on around us; a feeling of separation. For young people this can be very difficult to handle, especially if they don't feel secure in their existing relationships.

This activity is designed to generate situations in which everyone experiences the reactions of others without knowing their cause. It is intended to stimulate discussion based on individuals' feelings as a result of their experience. Though the activity is fun, for many it can come close to their everyday experiences of life in school and so will need careful and sensitive handling.

Objectives

- to experience how our feelings change according to the reactions of group members
- to experience being on the receiving end of other people's reactions

Materials

A class set of self-adhesive *Close encounter labels* each carrying a statement describing how the bearer should be treated by the rest of the group

Procedure

a Invite the class to spread themselves out around the room.
b Give out a self-adhesive label to each member of the class, still attached to its backing sheet.
c Invite the class to rapidly exchange their labels until they are told to stop, then *without looking at the label* peel it from its backing sheet and attach it to their foreheads.
d Invite the class to move around and react to each other according to the instruction on the label.

e From time to time (minimum of 2 minutes each time) stop the activity and invite volunteers to say what they think is written on their label.

f Judge from the reactions of the class and the energy being generated whether to continue the activity by inviting the class to exchange labels again without looking at the one they end up with.

g Invite the class to organise itself into groups of four or five and use the prompts to generate a round of personal statements as a basis for conversation.

Prompts for reflection

• The response I found most difficult to give was . . .
• I liked it least when people . . .
• I would have hated to . . .
• The ones I recognise from real life are . . .

Suggestions for follow-up work

1 Distribute labels so that each appears twice. Invite pupils to find their partner according to their similar reactions to each other.

2 Ask pupils to observe closely the facial expressions of newsreaders on the television and the people who are interviewed as part of the news. This should be done over a period of days. 'What do you notice about their use of a variety of facial expressions? Why do you think this happens? How do facial expressions affect us when we are faced with a group of people all looking the same?'

Close encounter labels

CHOICES

stare at me

frown at me

laugh at me

look through me

glance at me

tut tut at me

glare at me

grimace at me

laugh with me

nod to me

wonder at me

bow to me

smile at me

snigger at me

look away from me

wink at me

point at me

gently shake my hand

8.5 Role swopper

Our ability to cope with situations in which there is conflict relies to a great extent on our flexibility of response. This implies that different situations and circumstances need different responses. The capacity to vary our response is a product of past experience and mental agility.

This activity is designed to create a variety of situations in which individuals can rehearse their responses from both points of view. Exchanging roles is very important since it allows everyone to have the opportunity to 'stand in the other person's shoes'.

Objectives

- to provide the experience of being on both sides of a situation
- to see things from another person's point of view

Materials

Sets of *Role swopper situation cards* (one set per pair), each set in an envelope.

Procedure

a Invite the class to organise themselves into pairs.
b Pairs decide who is **A** and **B**.
c **A** opens the envelope, takes out a card and reads it aloud to **B**.
d **A** and **B** take on the roles described. (one minute)
e **A** and **B** now exchange roles. (one minute)
f Pairs discuss the situations using the prompts below.
g **A** passes the envelope to **B** who reads a card out to **A** and the procedure is repeated for each of the four cards.

Prompts for reflection (in groups of four)

- A true life situation I have been in similar to this was . . .
- For me the most difficult situation was . . .
- When we exchanged roles I . . .

- I laughed most when . . .
- What I have learned is . . .

Suggestions for follow-up work

Invite pupils to keep a record for a week of the situations they encounter that are clear-cut and two-sided. 'Either during or immediately after the encounter see if you can describe for yourself the other person's point of view. Does this have any effect on your position?'

Role swopper situation cards

CHOICES

A is wanting to sell

B is not wanting to buy

A is making too much noise

B is an annoyed neighbour

A is in a hurry to leave

B urgently wants to talk

A is aggressive

B is calm and controlled

8.6 Get out of that

This activity is designed to give pupils a variety of experiences that they may encounter in their everyday lives, as a basis for developing a flexibility of response. The process of reflection is particularly emphasised in an attempt to convert experience into learning. Finally the opportunity to devise situations from their own experience for another pair, reinforces the relevance of the activity and allows pupils to check out how someone else dealt with the same situation.

Objectives

- to increase the flexibility of spoken response
- to introduce ways for coping with pressure

Materials

One set of *Stem phrase cards* for each pair, in an envelope
One set of *Situation cards* for each pair

Procedure

a Ask the class to organise themselves into pairs seated in their own space.
b Each pair decides who is **A** and **B**.
c **A** opens the envelope and reads out the first selected card to **B**.
d **A** starts with phrase 1, **B** replies with phrase 2, **A** continues with 3 and **B** with 4. After this **A** and **B** improvise their own situation. (2 minutes)
e **A** and **B** decide on one sentence that sums up the situation they created.
f The envelope is passed to **B** and the procedure repeated once more.
g **A** and **B** attempt to see any patterns that appeared in the way they worked and fill in a *Situation card*.
h **A** and **B** exchange partners with another pair. Each pair now attempts to produce two new situation cards of their own, drawing on their own experiences in life.

i The associated pairs exchange self-produced cards to try out on each other.
j Pairs combine into fours to reflect on the activity, using the prompts below.
k Pairs who worked on the same initial prompts join together to compare their ideas and the conclusions they came to.

Prompts for reflection

• What this activity caused me to do was . . .
• The easiest part of the activity was . . .
• If you were the one who had to start the situation it meant . . .

Suggestions for follow-up work

1 Invite pupils to build up a collection of stem phrases and see which ones people can associate with in their everyday lives.
2 Repeat the activity under different conditions:
   • pairs seated side by side
   • pairs seated opposite each other
   • pairs standing very close
   • pairs separated by two metres
   • both partners' hands tied behind their backs
   • partners blindfolded
   • a pair against an individual
   • a larger group against an individual

Stem phrase cards

CHOICES

A: I don't think you should go.

B: You know that I have to.

A: I don't think you should go.

B: I have to.

A: Why did you do that?

B: I just felt like it.

A: You just felt like it.

B: Yes I just felt like it.

A: You can't afford that.

B: Yes I can.

A: No you can't afford that.

B: Yes I can afford it.

A: Why did you choose a red one?

B: It seemed the best choice.

A: But why a red one?

B: It was the best for the job.

Situation card

CHOICES

Original situation
A
B
A
B

Ideas developed by A	Ideas developed by B

Conclusion reached

Single sentence summary

8.7 Reds and blues

Teacher's notes

Young people are exposed to pressures from various groups to which they are expected to conform. For example, they may experience pressures directed at their appearance: individuals may be expected to dress in a certain way, to wear certain types of shoes, to have their hair cut in a particular style. Or group pressure may require individuals to spend their leisure time in specific ways: to meet at set times and in set places. Finally group members may be required to do certain things to join the group and maintain their place within it. Smoking, drinking and the use of drugs or solvents may be typical activities associated with group life.

This particular activity is designed to illustrate in a neutral way the situation described above. It offers individuals an insight into the choices before them in their own world and the decisions required.

Objectives

- to simulate the effects of pressure groups
- to give individuals the experience of being observers and reporters

Materials

Large sheets of paper/newsprint
Red and blue thick felt-tip pens
Red and blue paper
Red and blue hats, scarves, jumpers etc

Procedure

a Ask the class to form four equal-sized groups; the Reds, the Blues, the Observers and the Non-Aligned. (If you choose to allow the groups to form themselves remember that you must have six observers.)

b Reds and Blues work together in their separate groups to plan their strategies for persuading the Non-Aligned to join them. They may produce banners, slogans, jingles . . . anything they think appropriate. Each group is assigned space in the classroom.

c The Non-Aligned leave the room and discuss what it is like to be uninvolved in the Reds and Blues, in fact to be outside of any group. (A variation here is to separate the members of the Non-Aligned so that they do not perceive themselves as a group. In these circumstances they are asked to write 3 sentences about being non-aligned.)

d The Observers divide up equally between the other three groups. Those with the Reds and Blues must not speak or interfere in any way, merely observe and record what is happening. Those with the unaligned interview the members individually about the feelings of being Non-Aligned. (20 minutes)

e The Non-Aligned are led into the room to be subjected to pressure from the Reds and the Blues who take it in turn to express their case. They must decide to join one or the other, or justify remaining unaligned.

f The Observers report back to the groups they have observed.

g The simulation is debriefed and a list of strategies used by the Reds and Blues is built up and displayed.

h The whole class then brainstorms strategies for resistance.

Prompts for reflection (in pairs, then as a group)

- In our group we . . .
- If I could choose again the group I would join would be the . . . because . . .
- The ways we decided our strategies were . . .
- In the group I was in I said . . .
- As a Non-Aligned person I felt . . . when I came into the room
- In real life situations similar to this one . . .

Suggestions for follow-up work

1 With the pupils, build up a collection of similar real life situations – football followers; gangs; political groups – and work out their strategies for pressurising the individual.

2 Invite pupils to produce a 'spotter's guide' for detecting group pressure, and a list of strategies for dealing with it.

8.8 Story boards

Most pupils' experience of life includes encounters and situations about which they are unsure. The individuals may not have been personally involved; they might merely have been passive observers of other people's situations. Nevertheless these experiences are the raw material from which they learn about their values and attitudes, and construct a view of their options and circumstances.

This activity allows for an interplay between individuals' past experiences and the fruits of their imagination, as a basis for creating problem solving situations.

Objectives

- to produce a wide variety of dissimilar stories quickly
- to brainstorm solutions to situations

Materials

Class set of *Story board* sheets (page 233)

Procedure

a Ask the class to organise themselves into groups of four; each group sits around a table.
b Give out the *Story board* sheets and ask group members to write their names at the top.
c Explain that each group is to use their imagination and describe a situation in which one person is under pressure to do something he does not want to do.
d Groups discuss the situation and describe it in the top box on the sheet provided.
e The sheets are passed on to another group who read the opening statements then decide how to develop the storyline.
f The group writes the development in the next box down the page.
g The sheet is passed on for a second time and the procedure repeated.

h Finally the story sheet is returned to the original group who now read the development of their own story and 'tidy it up'.
i In turns, each group of four presents their finished version to the whole class who brainstorm solutions. The solutions are written up on a large sheet of paper.
j Finally the groups analyse the collected sets of solutions, and look for their common patterns.

Prompts for reflection

• The thing that surprised me about the stories was . . .
• One experience I have had of being pushed into something was . . .
• When I don't want to do what others want me to do I . . .

Suggestions for follow-up work

1 Invite groups to take the stories and develop them into role plays.
2 Focus on the consequences of alternative courses of action – divide the class into two groups to follow through a particular course of action to see where they think it would lead.
3 Ask the class to produce adventure stories: start from a single position stated in three sentences, divide up into two groups, each of which agree on three more sentences; each group divides again, now forming four groups which add three more sentences . . . and so on until the whole class is divided and individuals are working alone. Compare the end points reached by discussing them in groups of four, then as a class.

Story board sheet

Group members names

Initial situation

1st development of situation

2nd development of situation

Tidied-up version

Brainstorm solutions

9 Rights and responsibilities

'I know my rights!' may be a familiar cry and one which is not confined to the young, yet few people will assert with similar enthusiasm that 'I know my responsibilities!'. The tension between one's rights and one's responsibilities forms the focus of this chapter, and the activities examine issues which are likely to raise powerful emotions about freedom and justice.

Most young people wish to establish greater autonomy as they grow older and increased independence from their parents signals the approach of adulthood. Therefore, age is a significant factor when our ascribed or perceived rights and responsibilities are considered; other factors may include changing authority relationships, personal circumstances and status.

There are ways in which society seeks to protect its young through the application of legislation. In *When age is important*, one specific aspect of the law – the legality of young people of a particular age being involved or participating in certain activities – is examined. Having tested their existing knowledge of specific situations, pupils are encouraged to use local sources of information to check their accuracy and to investigate other activities which are affected by age-related laws.

9.1 When age is important

Rights and responsibilities are not solely a matter of moral judgment but may be governed by legislation. Thus, there is likely to be tension between opinions and facts in our daily experience. Rules and laws govern our actions and to ignore them may have adverse outcomes for ourselves and others. In this activity, the pupils are invited to consider aspects of the law relating to young people and to discuss their opinions as to the 'right answer'.

Pupils should not assume that because they agree upon a decision their collective response is necessarily correct. Neither should they become dependent upon you as the provider of answers to all factual questions. As part of the educative process young people should be encouraged to use other sources, for example, library, Citizens' Advice Bureau, Community Association and other statutory and voluntary bodies. They should see their community as a rich resource for their enquiries.

Information cards may help to establish pupils' current state of knowledge and form an aid for revision. The ability to identify relevant retrieval systems and have the confidence to use them is likely to be of increasing importance in a technological age.

Objectives

- to investigate pupils' knowledge about the legality of certain age-related activities
- to encourage pupils to use the reference services within and outside the school in order to check the accuracy of their knowledge relating to age-related activities

Materials

A set of *Rights and Responsibilities* cards (page 240) for each group of four pupils
Pencils

Procedure

a Divide the class into groups of four pupils; ideally, clustered around a table or desk.

b Give out a set of cards to each group. Explain that on each card there is a short statement relating to an activity which is governed by one's age, eg 'It is legal to purchase a pet ferret if you are over 9 years of age'.

c The 12 cards are placed face downwards in a stack. Each member in turn takes a card and reads out the statement on it. He offers an opinion as to whether or not the statement is 'true' or 'false'; other group members are asked if they support or disagree with the decision. Whatever the response, the group seeks to identify a place(s) where the statement could be checked and this information is written on the reverse of the card. *No-one draws the next card until the one in hand has been fully explored and a decision(s) reached.*

d The pupils mark the card in one of the following ways:
T . . . True (where *all* members agree)
F . . . False (where *all* members agree)
U . . . Uncertain (where members disagree)
and place the cards in piles for the three categories, on the table.

e Some groups will probably take longer than others. Those who finish early could compile a list of age-related issues for further investigation.

f Ask groups working in close proximity to combine to share their verdicts and identify places where they can check or clarify their decisions.

g Collect verbal responses to each card from the whole class, in terms of
• the correctness of their answers;
• the places where accurate information may be sought.

h Ask each group to agree upon a division of labour so that they can check the information by the next lesson (or by an agreed date). Groups could also gather information on other age-related issues.

Prompts for reflection

• I think I am the only person in this class who knows the age when . . .
• I would like to know the age when . . .

- Getting old means . . .
- I think adults would like to be my age again because . . .

Suggestions for follow-up work

1 Invite each group to design another set of 12 cards based on its particular enquiry; these could be used with another group in the class or other classes in the school.
2 Pupils could invite key personnel, for example, a member of the police force, who can provide answers to their enquiries about the legality of age-related activities. (See the section in Chapter 2 on the 'visitor technique', pages 30–31.)

Rights and responsibilities

You are allowed to buy fireworks when you are 12.

You are allowed to choose your own doctor when you are 16 years old.

You have to be 17 years old before you can buy alcoholic drinks in a bar.

If you are 13 years old, you are entitled to buy a pet animal.

You are entitled to enter a betting shop when you are 17.

You can join a trade union when you are 14 years old.

You are entitled to vote when you are 18.

You can enter into a hire purchase agreement when you are 17.

You can be held responsible for a crime when you are 14.

You are not allowed to purchase cigarettes under the age of 16.

You are able to marry, with your parents consent, when you are 16.

You have to be 15 years old before you are entitled to buy a gun.

9.2 Snowballing people

This activity is designed to provide young people with the experience of consensus seeking. As the group grows in size, it becomes increasingly difficult to obtain a consensus.

The issue selected is one about which young people are likely to hold a range of values; therefore, they will need to negotiate criteria by which they make judgments relating to rank order.

There is no particular significance in the occupations chosen (see page 243); you may wish to replace some or all with roles which may be more appropriate for your area. If a parent of a pupil in the class has one of the occupations it may be advisable to find a substitute in case this causes embarrassment or leads to adverse comment. An alternative would be to use the names of present-day celebrities, famous people of the past or cartoon characters.

Objectives

• to illustrate that consensus becomes more difficult to achieve as the number of people involved in the decision-making process increases
• to show that each person uses criteria which may be at odds with those of a colleague

Materials

One copy of the *Occupations sheet* for each pupil
Pencils

Procedure

a Divide the class into *eight* groups of similar numbers. Give each pupil an *Occupations sheet*. Invite pupils to write one of the eight occupations listed at the top of the sheet alongside each of the amounts of money. The figures represent the amount of money that a person doing each of the occupations *should* receive each week.

There must be only one occupation against one amount. If the sums of money become a major distraction, remove them and emphasise once again the purpose of the activity – to place the eight roles in order of relative importance within society.

b Give the groups five minutes in which to place the roles in rank order. If pupils complete the task ahead of schedule, they could compile a list of reasons as to the criteria they used.

c Ask groups to combine to form four new groupings and give a fresh *Occupations sheet* to each group. Using their previous records, members negotiate on a new agreed order. (5–10 minutes)

d Ask the groups to combine once again so that the two groups created each contain half of the total class. On a new sheet, each group renegotiates the rank order, using any of their earlier lists. The method by which an agreed order is reached is not important in this exercise. Because of the number of pupils involved, this may take up to 20 minutes; on some occasions, pupils may not be able to identify a priority order at all.

e Ask the groups to reveal their rank order. Then set up a debriefing session which focuses upon the ways in which group size aids or inhibits the achievement of consensus.

Prompts for reflection

- Every person in the world is entitled to . . .
- It was difficult to reach agreement because . . .
- I think that the idea of paying everybody the same weekly wage is . . .
- I value people who . . .

Suggestions for follow-up work

Invite pupils to develop an interview schedule for investigating the views of young people on the rights of one of the following categories: the disabled; the elderly; the homeless; the under-fives.

The class may wish to study *all* groups in order to identify those rights that are common.

Some pupils could contact local, regional and national statutory and voluntary bodies to obtain literature and support materials to assist in the identification of key issues relating to the four named categories.

Occupation sheet

CHOICES

Lawyer   Coal miner   Pilot   Refuse collector
Bricklayer   Doctor   Pop star   Politician

£800 . . . .
£700 . . . .
£600 . . . .
£500 . . . .
£400 . . . .
£300 . . . .
£200 . . . .
£100 . . . .

--✂

Lawyer   Coal miner   Pilot   Refuse collector
Bricklayer   Doctor   Pop star   Politician

£800 . . . .
£700 . . . .
£600 . . . .
£500 . . . .
£400 . . . .
£300 . . . .
£200 . . . .
£100 . . . .

9.3   Sounds great!

The opportunity to fantasise about the ideal school seems to be welcomed by many young people. Even the most enthusiastic pupils sometimes sigh 'If only . . . '. Some of their dreams may be desirable and attainable; others will remain figments of the imagination. Whatever the intention or motivation, fantasy can provide a rich resource for the learning process.

In this activity, pupils generate ideas through brainstorming, decide upon criteria and describe their ideal school in eight sentences. From the range of 'schools', pupils are invited to consider the suitability of a school, first for themselves in their current status and then – in the role of prospective parents – for their children. These two distinctive perspectives seek to highlight the rights and responsibilities one claims for oneself and on behalf of others.

Stress that no reference to any existing member of the school should be made, either directly or by inference as it may cause embarrassment. A large wall area should be available for the display of each group's work.

Objectives

- to identify the features of an ideal school
- to compare and contrast the views of pupils in terms of their current status and that of prospective parents

Materials

A piece of A4 lined paper for each group
Pencils
Sheets of newsprint
One thick felt-tip pen for each group
Masking tape or blu-tak
Copies of the example *Ideal school* (page 247)

Procedure

a Ask pupils to form groups of four. Each group agrees upon a scribe who will record the group's responses to the task. Issue each group with a piece of A4 lined paper, pencil, large sheet of newsprint and thick felt-tip pen.

b Ask the group to generate as many ideas as possible about their 'ideal school'. On the A4 paper, the scribe writes down *all* suggestions, even if there is disagreement between members. (5–7 minutes) Do not at this point mention the parental perspective of the task.

c Each group discusses its contributions and finally produces an agreed statement of no more than eight sentences on the features of an ideal school. (If pupils are experiencing difficulty, you could show them the example on page 247.) One member of each group writes the ideas in bold print on a large sheet of newsprint. (20–25 minutes)

   During the exercise, hand out blu-tak or masking tape to affix to the sheets of newsprint, and allocate a letter of the alphabet to each group, which is written clearly in the top right-hand corner of the sheet.

d Display the sheets around the walls – spaced out so that pupils can walk around to view them.

e Ask the members of each group to form pairs, labelled **A** and **B**. Pair **A** seek to identify the school they would like to attend as pupils. Pair **B** identify the school they would like their *children* to attend. The discussion between partners, as they consider their preferences, is an important part of the activity. Having identified their ideal school, pupils return to their original groups. (5–7 minutes)

f The group exchanges its views on the criteria members used to select their respective schools. In some cases, pairs may not have identified one particular school, but are likely to be able to discuss the features they valued or rejected in a number of schools.

g Pupils discuss the ways in which pupils' and parents' views may be at odds or in harmony.

Prompts for reflection

• I would never send my children to a school where . . .
• My ideal school would have . . .
• Parents have the responsibility to ensure that their child's school is . . .
• In school, children should have the right to . . .

Suggestions for follow-up work

1 Invite pupils to mount an enquiry among other pupils in the school into some of the issues raised during this lesson, in terms of their own or an ideal school.
2 The enquiry could be extended to include parents and adults in the community.

Example **Ideal School**

There are no bells. You can come to school if you wish but nobody chases you if you wish to stay away. There are no examinations. The teachers are referred to by their first names. You can use the school's cafeteria at any time of the day. Smoking is allowed on the tennis courts. No homework is set.

-->✂

There are no bells. You can come to school if you wish but nobody chases you if you wish to stay away. There are no examinations. The teachers are referred to by their first names. You can use the school's cafeteria at any time of the day. Smoking is allowed on the tennis courts. No homework is set.

1986   David Settle/Charles Wise   Basil Blackwell

9.4 Peeling the onion

Every day, we have to make hundreds of decisions relating to our own well-being and that of other people. Sometimes we respond instantaneously and appropriately to a familiar scene, relying upon intuition and past experience. However, on examination the complexities of a situation may reveal features which were not anticipated on first impressions.

To illustrate the dangers of making immediate judgments about a seemingly straightforward situation, eg a five-year-old boy crying on his way to and from school, 12 pieces of information are presented in sequence. As layers are exposed, more reasons may be deduced to explain the actions of the characters.

You need to assess carefully the amount of time required for pupils to consider each piece of information. To move on too quickly may destroy the developmental nature of the task, but a slow pace may lead to boredom and distraction.

Objectives

- to demonstrate that seemingly straightforward situations may be more complex than one had initially perceived

Materials

A set of 12 *Situation cards* (page 250) for each group of three or four

Procedure

a Divide the class into groups of three or four. Give each group a pile of 12 *Situation cards* which are placed face downwards on their table. Ask the group not to touch the cards. Explain that the cards are numbered from 1 to 12 inclusive, and the first card to be drawn will be number one. Pupils should take it in turns to take a card from the top of the pack, when you indicate that they do so.

b The first pupil in each group draws the top card and reads it to the other members. They discuss how they feel about this situation.

When you feel it is appropriate ask groups to move on to the next card.

c The second pupil draws the top card and the procedure is repeated until all cards have been used. (You may wish to check with individual groups as to the issues that are being raised.) (20–30 minutes)

d Pairs of groups join up to exchange views about the situation.

e Invite groups to view the situation through the eyes of Alan, his father or his mother and compare differences.

Prompts for reflection

• Alan was probably most upset by . . .
• I feel that Alan's mother was . . .
• I feel that Alan's father was . . .

Suggestions for follow-up work

Ask each group to identify a situation in which the perceived rights and responsibilities of young people and another member of the community come into conflict. They then devise 12 statements for cards which encapsulate the complexity of the situation.

Situation cards

1 Alan is five years old and has just started school. He previously enjoyed play group

2 Alan walks to and from school alone each day. He has to cross the road by the school

3 On most days, Alan cries on the way to and from school

4 Alan's father spends a great deal of time away from home

5 Alan's best friend has recently left the area

6 Alan's mother never takes him to school

7 Alan does not like school as he is afraid of the older children

8 Alan has no older brother or sister

9 Alan's mother had another child six months ago

10 Alan loves his brother and does not like leaving him each morning

11 Alan has been told that he will have to wear glasses

12 Alan is very happy at home and his friends come to play. He loves his family

9.5 Helping hand

There are numerous occasions when people need to work cooperatively in order to ensure the effective completion of a task. At times, members of a group need to negotiate an acceptable division of labour which accommodates each person's needs and strengths, to the satisfaction of all concerned. But there may be occasions when conflict results from the intransigence of one or more individuals.

Through role play, this activity focuses upon a domestic situation, where characters have to contribute to a collective task. Once they have adopted a specific role within the family grouping, individuals are free to demonstrate whatever viewpoints they believe their character might possess. The outcome of the role play cannot be predicted but it is likely that individuals will seek to ascertain and establish rights and responsibilities within the group.

The activity requires groups of four pupils; if it is not possible for all groups to be this size you will need to devise a method for identifying those who cannot be accommodated in the role play. For example, you might issue each pupil with a small piece of paper on which he or she writes a number from 1–99. Choose a number at random and ask which pupils have this number or one that is close. By this method, one or more pupils can be identified to act as 'observers'. The observer's role is to attach himself to one character within a group, and to note the behaviour of all the characters.

Objectives

• to examine the caring and selfish behaviour of individuals when faced with a collective task

Materials

One copy of the *Family situation* (page 254) for each pupil
One copy of *A Helping Hand* (page 255) for each pupil
Pencils

Procedure

a Invite pupils to volunteer to be observers. Divide the rest of the class into groups of four.

b In groups, members decide upon their respective roles within a family grouping. For those groups who have difficulty deciding upon roles you may wish to offer some examples (see Figure 9.a).

A – Father, Mother, Son, Daughter
B – Grandmother, Grandfather, Mother, Daughter
C – Mother, Daughter, Son, Son
D – Father, Son, Daughter, Daughter
E – Grandfather, Mother, Father, Son

Fig. 9.a Some examples of family groupings

The age of each character should be determined by the group but no person should be under 10 or over 70 years old. It should be assumed that all characters are in good health.

c Issue each character with a copy of the *Family situation*. As a private task, the character describes the stance he proposes to take. From this time, no discussion about the situation should take place until the start of the role play. Emphasise that pupils must remain in role until further notice.

d Within the group, pupils number themselves 1, 2, 3 and 4.

e Pupils playing roles 1 and 2 go to one end of the room, roles 3 and 4 to the other end. In role, pairs discuss the situation, while you move between pairs to monitor the work. (3–5 minutes)

f Stop the activity and ask pairs to reconvene in their family groups. Then repeat the procedure with 2 and 3 meeting in one area, 1 and 4 in another site. (3–5 minutes)

g 1 and 3 meet in one area, 2 and 4 in another site and repeat the procedure.

h After the final round of paired work, the family group meets and discusses *in role* how the situation is to be resolved. (10–15 minutes)

i Ask the pupils to de-role. In their groups, every pupil uses a copy of *A Helping Hand* to record examples of each character's selfish or caring behaviour. It is important that you emphasise that comments made must refer to the *character*, not to the individual who played the role. (10 minutes)

j Using the recorded material, each group decides how all parties could have contributed to the gardening task.

Prompts for reflection

- The best example of cooperation in the role play was between . . .
- The character who caused trouble did so because . . .
- From this role play, I learnt . . .
- The best example of pupils working together in this school is . . .

Suggestions for follow-up work

1 As an individual activity, invite pupils to note the behaviour of people engaged in a collective task within their neighbourhood. The activity sheets used in the lesson may be adapted for use outside school. Within the groups of four established for the role play each pupil reports his findings. The group seeks to identify and record the conditions which a enhance and b inhibit the successful completion of a collective task.

2 Ask the class to mount an enquiry into the range of self-help groups within the community, with particular reference to the ways in which they accept responsibility for their actions and provide support for members.

3 Invite the class to consider a situation where a new family is moving into 'the house next door'. What needs will they have? How could you – the neighbours – help?

Family situation

The family has just moved into a new house on an estate. Both the front and back gardens are small. There is a considerable amount of builder's rubble to be cleared from the back garden before the family can plant vegetables, shrubs and flowers.

The family has just moved into a new house on an estate. Both the front and back gardens are small. There is a considerable amount of builder's rubble to be cleared from the back garden before the family can plant vegetables, shrubs and flowers.

The family has just moved into a new house on an estate. Both the front and back gardens are small. There is a considerable amount of builder's rubble to be cleared from the back garden before the family can plant vegetables, shrubs and flowers.

The family has just moved into a new house on an estate. Both the front and back gardens are small. There is a considerable amount of builder's rubble to be cleared from the back garden before the family can plant vegetables, shrubs and flowers.

A helping hand

	Examples of selfish behaviour	*Examples of caring behaviour*
Character 1 Role		
Character 2 Role		
Character 3 Role		
Character 4 Role		

9.6 Who is being unreasonable?

In this activity, pupils are asked to identify situations where they or their peers have responded to a request for assistance or help by saying 'Why should I?'. Given that the intonation of voice together with non-verbal signals may vary from person to person, this challenging question may be viewed as an act of defiance, hostility, indifference, or reluctance. Even where the young person may view a demand as unreasonable, the use of an assertive rather than aggressive response may enable both parties to feel that neither has 'lost face'.

Through the use of role play, pupils are invited to consider which party is behaving in an unreasonable way in a given situation, ie is it the person who requests help or the person who refuses to respond to the request?

In the section *Suggestions for follow-up* the portrayal of conflict by the media provides a useful extension to self-reported incidents.

Objectives

- to investigate ways in which people behave unreasonably
- to identify some of the characteristics of unreasonable behaviour
- to identify assertive rather than aggressive responses which may be made to demands to which one does not wish to or cannot respond

Materials

One piece of A4 paper for each small group
Pencils

Procedure

a Invite pupils to form an even number of groups containing four to six members.

b In groups, invite pupils to recall situations where they responded to a request from an adult to undertake a particular task by saying 'Why should I?' (or something similar). If pupils have not responded in this way, they may wish to offer examples from their observation of other people's behaviour.

c Groups appoint one member as scribe to record the contributions. (5–7 minutes)
d Invite each group to select *one* of the situations for closer scrutiny. The pupil (referred to as the 'provider') who offered the situation gives a detailed description of how events unfolded and developed.
e From these details, the group devises a role play which captures the emotions of the various characters involved in the situation. Explain that the role play will be shown to one other group. (You may need to help particular groups with this.) The provider does not take a role but ensures that the events leading up to and following the query 'Why should I?' are consistent with the situation he recalled earlier. (15 minutes)
f Ask groups to join in pairs, identified as **A** or **B** within the new grouping. Ask the new groups to find space to work in.
g Group **A** performs its role play. Members of group **B** consider their responses to the question 'Who is being unreasonable?'.
h After the role play, members of group **A** de-role and group **B** offers its response to the question and members justify the stance they have taken. Group **A** members may wish to offer their observations.
i Group **B** perform the role play for Group **A** to observe, and group **A** consider their responses to the question, as previously.
j Invite the class to reassemble and brainstorm responses to the sentence: 'If someone asks me to do something, instead of saying 'Why should I?', I could say . . . ' Encourage pupils to consider how an assertive rather than an aggressive response may be offered when unreasonable demands are made.

Prompts for reflection

- I behave well when . . .
- I behave badly when . . .
- I respond well to people who are . . .
- I respond badly to people who are . . .

Suggestions for follow-up work

1 In small groups, invite pupils to draw a cartoon which illustrates a conflict situation, and show it to another small group in the class. The designers then present a role play *or* the receiving group presents a role play, based upon their interpretation of the perceived situation.

2 Ask each pupil to bring in two photographs from magazines and newspapers which show two or more people engaged in a conflict situation. In groups of four to six, members place the photographs in rank order according to the seriousness of the conflict; an agreed order has to be negotiated.

Another group is invited to view the photographs while a member of the presenting group offers a justification for the rank order.

3 Ask small groups to collect copies of six different daily newspapers on sale on the same day. Each group identifies one article that addresses the same issue in all (or most) of the newspapers. Members are asked to see if the issue is reported similarly in all the papers; if not, why not?

9.7 Persuasion

Persuasion takes many forms and may induce either negative or positive behaviour. In this activity, you should state that although a range of persuasive techniques is available, the use of abusive language and physical violence is not permitted. In *Situation 1* the persuader attempts to encourage positive behaviour, whereas in *Situations 2* and *3* negative modes of behaviour are sought.

In pairs, pupils engage in role play, while an observer notes the ploys used by the persuader. The presence of an observer may enhance or limit the learning experience, so you should consider the effect upon the characters involved. One point of view suggests that an observer inhibits the participants, particularly if he takes notes during the role play. However, a contrary view highlights the key role the observer plays in providing information for the post-play analysis.

Within a trusting environment, the activity may help pupils develop their powers of observation and, through discussion, enable them to devise schemes for future occasions.

Objectives

- to explore the ways in which young people attempt to persuade their peers

Materials

One set of *Role sheets* for each group
Pencil and a sheet of A4 lined paper for one member of each group

Procedure

a Ask the class to form groups of three and label themselves **A**, **B** and **C** within each group. Distribute the role cards for *Situation 1* – role **A** to person **A**; role **B** to person **B** and role **C** to person **C**. Explain that pupils are not to discuss or show their role details to anyone else. Each pupil should take on his role, and remain in that role until further notice. (If there are more than three in any group, the additional member should also act as an observer – role **C**.)

b Each pupil reads through his role. Make sure everyone understands what they are to do. (3 minutes)

c A and B engage in conversation while person C observes and records details. (If the observer has writing difficulties, ask him to try to remember what happens.)

d When you judge that sufficient time has elapsed, stop the conversation. (The role play may last from 2–5 minutes. The duration should be the same for all groups, so that exchanges are not interrupted at various stages. Once you stop the conversation, it is inadvisable to try to re-start it.)

e Ask pupils to de-role and re-establish their own persona. Invite the observers (C) to report back to their groups, commenting on the way in which person A sought to persuade person B. It should be made clear to all pupils that the observer is talking about their exchanges *when they were in role*. (3–5 minutes)

f A and B are asked to share their views about the feelings they experienced while playing their respective roles. (10 minutes)

g Within each group the observer draws two columns on the paper provided – one headed 'A tried to persuade B by . . . ' and the other 'B tried to resist A by . . . '. You may wish to write these details on the blackboard. Groups then fill in the columns. (5 minutes)

h Two or three groups join up to compare notes. (10 minutes)

Prompts for reflection

- I don't always do what others want me to do because . . .
- I don't like people who . . .
- Sometimes my friends try to persuade me to . . .
- I think I would always try to persuade my friends to . . .

Suggestions for follow-up work

1 In the same roles (ie A, B and C) invite the class to explore other situations where friends or peers exert pressure (see Situations 2 and 3, page 261). Both examples may be used to consider how one resists negative peer pressure.

2 The class may wish to investigate and compare the pressures exerted by the friends of pupils in other years.

3 The media exert subtle pressure on young people to buy particular items such as fashions and drinks. Ask the class to investigate how advertising agencies promote products in the market place. They may go on to question the morality of persuading young people to behave in a particular way.

Role sheet

CHOICES

*Person **A** – Situation 1* (I start the conversation)

I wish to persuade my friend to join me in a 20-mile sponsored walk for Save the Children Fund. I make every effort to gain his/her agreement and will not give in.

---

*Person **B** – Situation 1*

I do not wish to join my friend on a 20-mile sponsored walk for charity. I resist all his/her attempts to persuade me to take part. I keep thinking up reasons for not walking.

---

*Person **C** – Situation 1*

I am an *observer*. I do not become involved in the conversation but record the ways in which A tries to persuade B to take part in a sponsored walk.

---

*Person **A** – Situation 2*

I am an *observer*. I do not become involved in the conversation but record the ways in which B tries to persuade C not to do his/her homework.

---

*Person **B** – Situation 2* (I start the conversation)

I dislike doing homework and also want my friend to refuse to do it. I am willing to use different means to persuade my friend.

---

*Person **C** – Situation 2*

I am keen to do well at school. I always do my homework and will resist any attempts to persuade me not to do it. I will not give in.

---

*Person **A** – Situation 3*

I have never tried a cigarette. I do not wish to smoke. I will resist my friend's attempts to change my mind.

---

*Person **B** – Situation 3*

I am an *observer*. I do not become involved in the conversation but record the ways in which C tries to persuade A to smoke.

---

*Person **C** – Situation 3* (I start the conversation)

I am a smoker. I wish to persuade my friend to smoke by using many different arguments.

9.8 Gerry Cunningham

This simulation provides pupils with the opportunity to examine the complexities relating to the rights and responsibilities of characters involved with a boy who is in trouble with the law. The exercise centres around interviews conducted by probation officers who are attempting to prepare a report prior to Gerry's court appearance. Probation officers usually work with clients on a one-to-one basis but the exercise has been designed so that a pair or small group may work together.

The exercise is best conducted in a hall, drama studio or other large uncluttered area.

Read the simulation carefully and anticipate enquiries that may be made concerning the role of the probation officer and the range of possible court sentences (see the list on page 266). It would be most helpful if a probation officer were available to answer queries during the work session.

It is important to be aware of any possible links between the characters and pupils in the class that may lead to distress or embarrassment. If character names are unsuitable they may be changed, as may some of the detail about one or more characters and the background information.

In the simulation conflicting evidence is presented by role holders. It is important for young people to realise that each person sees a similar situation from a different perspective and that tensions arise from this. We are frequently required to cope with ambiguity in our lives.

Figure 9.b shows the way chairs should be set out for the simulation. It will save time if this is done before the class arrives.

The exercise will require a minimum of one hour to ensure that there is adequate time for debriefing and reflection. Opportunities provided during the post-play session will reinforce and reiterate the points gained through the simulation.

Objectives

* to show how our judgments relating to a particular person or situation may alter on the receipt of more information
* to assess conflicting information from a range of sources

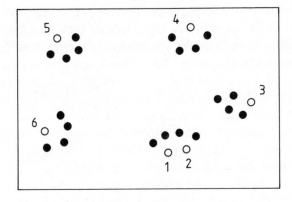

O – pupils who play the numbered roles

● – pupils who play Role 7 – Probation Officer

Fig. 9.b Layout for simulation

Materials

Pencils
For each pupil:
One copy of the *Background sheet* (page 266)
One copy of *Gerry Cunningham* (page 267)
For six pupils:
One set of *Role sheets* (pages 268–270)
For all remaining pupils:
One copy of *Role Sheet 7 – Probation Officer* (page 270)
A sheet of lined paper

Procedure

a Each pupil will play a specific role in this simulation, which focuses upon the life of Gerry Cunningham. Give each pupil a copy of the *Background sheet* so that he becomes familiar with the details surrounding Gerry's forthcoming court appearance. Explain that more details relating to the situation will be revealed during the simulation.

b Give each pupil the sheet headed *Gerry Cunningham*. Pupils record privately, under the column *Before*, the *one* most likely court ruling. You may need to explain the penalties in order to assist the pupils with their decision. On completion, the pupil retains this paper.

c Invite volunteers or identify pupils who are to play the six characters. Give each character his role together with a badge bearing the
   name. Ask pupils to read their roles carefully so that they become
   immersed in the character. The six characters remain in the room
   while you issue the details of *Role 7 – Probation Officer* to the rest of
   the pupils.

d All pupils study their roles but *do not discuss* them with each other.
   (5 minutes) The 'probation officers' may wish to formulate some
   questions on the lined paper provided (subsequently, they may
   wish to make notes during or after interviews).

e Characters take their seats and will remain in the same site throughout the exercise (see Figure 9.b on page 263). Allocate individuals,
   pairs or small groups to each site to start the questioning of a
   character.

f After five minutes stop the activity. Characters collect in one area of
   the room to discuss their feelings about the first round of interviews. The probation officers may only talk to members of their
   own group or to their partner. Emphasise to the characters that they
   should maintain their *own* perspective and not be swayed in successive interviews by comments from the probation officers that impli-
   citly or explicitly indicate a mismatch of information between
   characters.

g The characters return to their original positions. Ask the probation
   officers to move one place to their left and to interview the next
   character. (5 minutes)

h Repeat the procedure until all probation officers have interviewed
   each character.

i After the last round of interviews, all pupils de-role and focus upon
   the sheet headed *Gerry Cunningham*. Under the heading *After*, each
   pupil records his private response to the most likely outcome of
   Gerry's court appearance.

j Ask the class 'How many people have a different response in the
   Before and *After* columns?' It is usual to find that over 50% of pupils
   have changed their responses following the interviews.

k Ask pupils to consider why people's opinions change. The answer
   often relates to the fact that they have gained more information
   about the situation.

l Finish the activity with unstructured small group discussion.

Prompts for reflection

- When I interviewed him, I thought that Gerry's behaviour was . . .
- The most responsible person I interviewed was . . .
- The person who cared least about Gerry was . . .
- I think Gerry should . . .

Suggestions for follow-up work

This activity may be used as an introduction to work related to 'crime and punishment'. Pupils could collect information relating to criminal offences, arrange interviews with law enforcement officers and study the portrayal of criminal behaviour by the media.

Background sheet

Characters involved in the enquiry

1 Gerry Cunningham – 14 years old

2 Joyce Cunningham – Gerry's mother

3 Mike Cunningham – Gerry's father

4 Brian Cunningham – Gerry's brother

5 Elizabeth Smith – Gerry's Head of House

6 Ron Gillerby – Youth Club Leader

7 Probation Officer – role played by all other class members

Situation

Gerry has recently appeared in the Juvenile Court charged with vandalising an adventure playground by sawing through the wooden supports of a viewing tower. He is accused of causing £500 worth of damage.

The case has been adjourned for three weeks so that a probation officer can compile a report for the court.

Eighteen months ago, Gerry was given a police caution for breaking six windows on a new housing estate; five months ago he was given a second police caution after stealing cigarettes and sweets worth £2 from a local shop.

Gerry's brother, Brian (21) lived at home until he married Janice two months ago – they live in a flat nearby.

Gerry goes to the Youth Club every Tuesday and Friday. On Sundays, he plays football for the Club in the youth league.

Gerry Cunningham

Having read the background sheet, what do you think the court is likely to decide.

PLEASE TICK ONE

	Before	*After*
1 Absolute discharge (conviction, but no punishment)	☐	☐
2 Conditional discharge (from six months to three years)	☐	☐
3 Fine of £400 maximum (parents have to pay)	☐	☐
4 Fine of £400 maximum *plus* compensation (maximum of £2,000 parents to pay)	☐	☐
5 Attendance centre (12 × 2 hours each Saturday afternoon; run by police)	☐	☐
6 Detention centre (three weeks – six months)	☐	☐
7 Youth custody (four – six months)	☐	☐
8 Care order (Gerry removed from home)	☐	☐
9 Deferred sentence (Gerry's behaviour will be watched over the next few months – (maximum of six months) – he will then be recalled to court)	☐	☐
10 Supervision with an order for intermediate treatment	☐	☐

Role Sheet

Role Sheet 1 – Gerry Cunningham

I am being interviewed with my mother. Whatever questions are asked, I will not answer them; I will look at my mother and get her to answer for me.

If anyone annoys me, I will tell them that they are 'like all the rest, always picking on me'.

There is no way in which I will be helpful.

-->✂

Role Sheet 2 – Joyce Cunningham

I am being interviewed with Gerry.

I am 46 years old and work part-time for a local engineering company as a filing clerk. I take home £54 a week. I love Gerry but he is sometimes difficult to manage. He has always been the same. He tells me he wants to be 'put away' because he hates his father. I know he would do anything for me. He's a good boy.

My husband, Mike, used to hit him for being cheeky nearly every day but Gerry's too big now.

If Gerry is taken away from home, I will leave my husband. I have been in hospital on a number of occasions and if Gerry is taken away that's the end for me. I am desperate.

The teachers hate him. They say he plays truant but that's a lie. His brother hates him; he used to hit Gerry for no reason at all. I am the only person who understands Gerry. I don't know what the Court should do about Gerry, but they are not going to put him away.

My husband gives me £35 a week for housekeeping. I don't know how much he earns.

Role Sheet 3 – Mike Cunningham

I am 46 and work as an engineer at Alconness. I take home £140 per week after stoppages.

Gerry is spoilt by his mother; she cannot control him. I only have to shout at him and he does as he is told. I have never hit him. Gerry was afraid of his brother; they were always quarrelling.

I think Gerry should be taken away and given a stern lesson. I think Gerry needs to grow up and behave properly. Gerry is always wanting money and his mother gives in to him. I will be glad when Gerry starts work. School is too soft; he ought to be caned every time he plays truant. Gerry is lazy and scruffy. If he doesn't go away, my wife will be back in hospital again. I pay the rent, £29 per week. My wife brings home £54 a week.

---✂

Role Sheet 4 – Brian Cunningham

My brother is a 'Mummy's boy'. Gerry is weak, lazy and untidy. He is a thief and used to always be taking money from my bedroom. I used to give him a good hiding, but he's got worse.

He can come to live with us, but he will have to behave himself. My wife feels sorry for Gerry and thinks he needs a lot of love. My mother has a history of mental trouble and Gerry is too much for her. Gerry ought to be flogged. I used to go to the same school as Gerry and was in Mrs Smith's House. I didn't like her.

© 1986   David Settle/Charles Wise   Basil Blackwell

Role Sheet 5 – Elizabeth Smith

I have never met Mr and Mrs Cunningham. They do not come to Parents' Evenings. They do not answer letters about Gerry's poor behaviour, his truancy, his failure to do homework and his abuse towards teachers. Gerry is a bully. I placed him in Headmaster's detention three times last term for various offences, but he is getting worse. Gerry is difficult to talk with but he says he loves his mother very much and says his father is unkind to her. Gerry says he will never leave his mother. Gerry's brother, Brian, used to be in my House and he was a violent person.

Role Sheet 6 – Ron Gillerby

I feel sorry for Gerry. I have never met his parents but I am told his father is always in the pub. Gerry talks a lot about his mother and loves her very much, but he never talks about his father. I have never met his brother, Brian.

Gerry plays table tennis and snooker. He is a very good goalkeeper, probably the best one in the local league; he never misses a game.

Gerry looks under-nourished and untidy. He is on the club committee and serves in the Tuck Shop. He is trustworthy and reliable.

I think Gerry is a great asset to this club but feel he needs firm guidance.

Role Sheet 7 – Probation Officer

I will talk with all the characters so that I can write a court report. I will ask questions that hopefully will give me some vital information about Gerry.

Note: One probation officer would normally interview characters on his own and not in the company of other officers.

10 Problem page

In many teenage magazines, there is a problem page in which an Agony Aunt responds to young people's letters on a range of issues.

Some young people use this facility to seek advice and guidance on matters which they feel cannot be dealt with by those who are emotionally close to them. They may believe that to present the problem to a near relative or a parent would be to cause distress, embarrassment and shock or lead to a breakdown of relationships; whether or not their perceptions are well-founded is irrelevant. The need to preserve anonymity may be another reason for turning to an outside agency.

One of the difficulties of being presented with a problem in written form rather than through a face-to-face meeting is that we cannot be sure that the problem as expressed represents the major concern of the young person. Many teachers will be familiar with this situation through their work with pupils in a pastoral setting. With time and a clear indication that the teacher is listening and understanding, the pupil may eventually feel confident enough to reveal his *real* worry.

In this chapter, we present activities which focus upon issues and problems identified by young people. It is hoped that through discussion, pupils will see members of their class as people whom they can trust, not only with other people's problems, but also with their own. Of course there will remain issues upon which young people need to refer to other sources. Some problems need immediate resolution or a professional opinion, therefore pupils should be aware of the range of statutory and voluntary help agencies within the community, for example, telephone links and 'drop-in' centres.

In *Dear Vera*, groups of pupils apply their collective wisdom to letters sent to an Agony Aunt and consider what might be an appropriate response. The activity emphasises the need to consider the possible effects of advice that is offered, and that there is probably not a definitive answer to every problem.

The inevitability of conflict in close relationships is explored in *Areas of disagreement* where the focus is on parent-child interactions. What may be perceived as the unreasonable behaviour of parents is examined in *If I were a parent* . . . The issue of the rights and responsibilities of both parties is examined in these two activities.

Sometimes we are called upon to make an instant response, however provisional or tentative it may be, so in *Family carousel* pupils are faced with a battery of questions in quick succession.

The extent to which we should share our problems with another person is considered in *Learning to share*. It is important for pupils to realise that they may be vulnerable if they seek the support of those who cannot be trusted; the consequences of misplaced trust may have a devastating effect upon our lives.

Designed to help looks at how we identify people who may benefit from our help even before they come to us with a problem. Unfortunately, the rhetoric of the teenage years tends to describe adolescence as being problematic rather than as an important developmental stage through which the majority of young people pass unscathed. So that pupils do not become overburdened with the view that their lives represent a catalogue of problems, *Good things* focuses upon boys' and girls' perceptions about the positive features of belonging to their respective sexes.

The final activity *Is this me?* encourages pupils to reflect, through the use of self-perception scales, upon their ability to help themselves and others. An opportunity is provided for classmates to offer their view of each other's attributes (clearly this exercise requires good relationships between pupils). Through the experience of working on such materials, it is hoped that pupils will develop greater powers of empathy and sympathy.

10.1 Dear Vera

Sometimes it is difficult to seek the help of a close friend or relative, for fear of embarrassment or upset; instead we may turn to a person with whom we have no emotional ties.

The examples of letters written to Vera (pages 276–277) are transcribed from originals written by 13-year-old boys and girls, and have been selected as representative of a range of issues. In the activity, pupils are invited to select one of the six letters to analyse in depth. Then, within a small group, they pool their collective wisdom in order to frame an appropriate response. One or more of the letters may be replaced by others you feel are particularly relevant, while maintaining the procedure outlined in the text. However, letters used in the exercise should not relate to any member of the class, directly or by inference, unless a high level of mutual understanding has already been established.

Often problems which are publicly presented have much deeper roots. With this in mind, you could encourage pupils to extrapolate the hidden messages within a letter and to reflect upon the state of mind of the writer. It is important to emphasise the care we must take when offering advice to another person. Prefacing remarks with 'Well, you ought to . . . ' is directive, whereas 'You may wish to consider . . . ' may encourage reflection prior to action.

The activity may help pupils realise that seemingly straightforward problems do not always warrant immediate or definitive answers. It is also worth pointing out that one of the weaknesses of a response from an Agony Aunt is that without further details of the individual(s) involved in the stated situation, her reply is likely to be confined to points of generality.

The exercise may be curtailed at any stage, to be considered again on the next occasion that the pupils meet.

Objectives

- to analyse the request being made in a letter to an Agony Aunt
- to prepare a sympathetic response to someone who seeks help

Materials

A copy of the six *Dear Vera* letters (pages 276–277) for each pupil
A copy of the *Question Sheet* (page 278) for each pupil

Procedure

a Invite pupils to form groups of three to six. Give each pupil a copy of the six *Dear Vera* letters. When members have read them, ask each group to agree on the one which it finds most interesting. (10–12 minutes)

b The group acts as the Agony Aunt for their chosen letter. To help them formulate a response, give each pupil a copy of the *Question Sheet* (page 278).

c Each group chooses one member to act as scribe. Group members share their ideas and the scribe writes down their answers to each question in note form, using a single word or phrase for each item. These notes are for the private use of the group. Each group works independently. (You may wish to set time boundaries for one or more of the questions on the sheet, in order to maintain the focus and pace of the lesson.) (20–25 minutes)

d When the groups have completed their responses, ask if any group has written a different answer for Question 3 from the one they gave for Question 4. If so, ask the group to suggest reasons *why* the answer desired by the writer might differ from the answer given to make him feel better or avoid hurting his feelings.

e Invite groups who have selected the same letter to share their responses in a larger grouping. Groups who have selected different letters could compose a response in rough draft.

f If time permits, each separate group could write a response and these letters could be the subject for a further enquiry into how one writes to someone who has presented a problem.

Prompts for reflection

• I think that people who write to an Agony Aunt are . . .
• I think an Agony Aunt could help people of my age because . . .
• My ideal Agony Aunt is someone who . . .
• I would write a letter to an Agony Aunt if . . .
• I would never write to an Agony Aunt because . . .

Suggestions for follow-up work

1 Ask pupils to look through magazines for teenagers to see if they have an Agony Aunt column. Pupils could construct a pie-chart to display the prevalence of particular issues raised.

2 Two or three pupils could write to the Agony Aunts of different magazines. While they wait for a reply, other class members could respond to the letters. The class then compares its advice with that offered by the professionals. Some parents, teachers and older pupils may be willing to respond (perhaps anonymously) to the letters, in order to extend the possibilities for comparison.

Dear Vera

Letter 1 (boy)

Dear Vera,

I have taken up motorcross and have got a brilliant bike but everyone keeps laughing at me. They think I'm weird.

I can't take much more, I feel like killing myself or hitting them hard.

I'm not much good at motorcross but its my hobby.

Please help me.

Gary

Letter 2 (girl)

Dear Vera,

I've got a problem. I duno wot do do abot it cos I canot spel.

Help me now.

Lou

Letter 3 (boy)

Dear Vera,

My mum and dad don't think I'm very good at anything. They think my older brothers and sisters are all right.

They never talk to me unless they tell me off or tell me to do something.

I want them to notice me.

I don't like living at home, but there's nowhere else to go.

Yours hopefully

Mike

CHOICES

Letter 4 (girl)

Dear Vera

I have a problem. There is a really nice boy in my class at school. He has been going out with one of my friends and now he has packed her in. I am trying to make him notice me but he doesn't seem to have picked up the hint. Sometimes he smiles at me or waves but he has never asked me out. Please could you tell me what I am doing wrong, because I really like him. He is not much older than me and he has not asked any other girls out.

Yours

Anu

Letter 5 (boy)

Dear Vera

I am having trouble about my homework. I do it very well and the teachers are always pleased, so I get high marks. But the other children laugh and call me brain-box.

Please help

Yours

Errol

Letter 6 (girl)

Dear Vera

I find relating to people harder and harder as I get older. I find it difficult to mix with people or even to just have a conversation with somebody. I don't think it's because I'm shy but more because I just don't like human beings anymore. They are so cruel to each other and to other living creatures. I know that when I get older I must change or I will end up friendless. What should I do?

Yours sincerely

Joanne

1986   David Settle/Charles Wise   Basil Blackwell

Question sheet

CHOICES

1 How does the writer feel?	2 What does the writer want to know?
3 What does the writer want me to say?	4 What will I say in order to make the writer feel better?

10.2 Areas of disagreement

Even in the happiest families there are times when disagreements occur between members. In this activity, pupils identify and examine the issues over which they come into conflict with their parents.

On some issues, all pupils may share similar experiences, whereas there may be many more situations where there is variation. Factors such as age, culture, finance, gender and religion, as well as the hopes and fears of individuals, may underlie the way in which family members relate. The complexity of human relationships may be revealed as pupils discuss their unique view of life within the family.

In undertaking this activity you need to be sensitive to pupils who are adopted, fostered or who have lost a parent, as the role play may cause distress in some cases. However, if a trusting environment has been developed with the class, you may feel confident that pupils will show sensitivity to each other's personal circumstances.

In the suggested role play, pupils are asked to portray a common conflict situation between a child and a parent, and to suggest ways in which the dispute may be amicably resolved. This focus may be unfamiliar to some children who, in real life, always find themselves in the role of loser. Such insights may alert pupils to the realisation that one day they may be parents, and that pinning the blame on either party may be inappropriate.

Objectives

- to identify areas of disagreement between parents and children
- to examine one situation in which all pupils in a group find themselves in conflict with their parents

Materials

A set of three labelled *Importance* cards for each group (see Figure 10a)
20 blank cards *or* a set of prepared *Issues* cards (see page 282) for each group
A piece of A4 lined paper for each group
Pencils

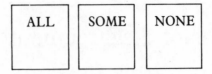

Fig. 10a Importance cards

Procedure

a Begin by saying something like 'Within all families there are likely to be occasions when members express disagreement on one or more issues.'

Using the brainstorming technique, the class generates a list of 18–20 issues on which young people and parents may disagree. (3–5 minutes)

(Alternatively, you may wish to use the 18 prepared *Issues* cards, see page 282.)

b Pupils organise themselves into groups of four or five. Give each group a set of cards corresponding to the number of issues recorded. Members copy one item on to each card. (It is helpful for each group to have a table or work surface.)

c Give each group three different-coloured *Importance* cards (see Figure 10.a above). These act as the headings for columns in a card-sorting exercise.

d Using the cards completed in b, pupils identify those which contain issues upon which *all* members have disagreements with their parents, and place these cards under the ALL heading. For issues where one or more members disagree with their parents, the cards are placed under the SOME heading. For issues where none of the members come into conflict with their parents, the cards are placed under NONE. (8–10 minutes)

e Groups change places to see how another group has sorted the cards. (3–4 minutes)

f Ask the groups to return to their original places. Each group selects one of the issues in the ALL column as the subject for a role play. If there are no issues in this category, the group may select from the SOME column.

g Group members form two sub-groups to look at the same issue. They discuss how the disagreement will be portrayed in the role play, so that the implications for both the young person and the parent(s) are clearly illustrated. Set a time deadline of 10–15 minutes for each group to develop and produce its role play.

h Within each group, one sub-group presents its situation, the other tries to identify ways in which the conflict could be amicably resolved.
i You may wish to invite sub-groups to show their role play to the class.

Prompts for reflection

- The best thing about being a member of a family is . . .
- I think I could help my parents more if . . .
- At home, I sometimes get angry because . . .
- In the family, boys get a better deal than girls because . . .

Suggestions for follow-up work

1 Invite the class to identify the most prevalent issues on which young people come into conflict with their parents. Pupils form small groups and each group chooses one issue to be considered. The group records on paper any possible events, flashpoints and incidents which may lead to conflict between the parties.

When the list has been compiled, the group examines every item and suggests a strategy which a member may adopt in order to defuse the situation.

After two or three weeks, the class may be invited to reflect upon any strategies that have been used and to consider the appropriateness and effectiveness of their actions.

2 Suggest that the class produces a *Guide for Parents: a young person's view*. Through action research amongst young people and parents, pupils may ascertain the issues to be included in the publication.

This major project would involve the negotiation of a division of labour among the pupils to encompass all aspects of the guide's preparation, presentation and distribution. Pupils may wish to seek financial support from outside the school and to market their product in the local community.

Issues

CHOICES

HOUSEWORK	TV PROGRAMMES
GARDENING	SCHOOL WORK
HOMEWORK	HAIRSTYLE
BEDTIME	COMING-IN TIME
FRIENDSHIPS	POLITICS
RELIGION	MONEY
BEHAVIOUR	BROTHER(S)
SISTER(S)	GRANDPARENT(S)
CLOTHES	TIDINESS

10.3 If I were a parent

In the previous two activities, the nature of relationships between children and parents was considered. In this activity, pupils are provided with an opportunity to engage in 'crystal ball gazing' in terms of how they believe they will behave as parents.

Inevitably there is a danger that the models of parenting presented as ideals by the pupils will invoke comparison with the actual behaviour of their parents. At the outset, you should stress that this activity can be conducted satisfactorily without any discussion of the way in which *their* parents behave. There is no obligation to 'reveal all' and by presenting a hypothetical situation, the likelihood of offence being caused to any individual's parents may be reduced.

Within a class one is likely to find a range of views on parenting, particularly in a multiethnic environment. This diversity of experience provides a rich resource for promoting greater tolerance and understanding of each other's cultures. During this work, pupils may discuss some of the tensions of growing up in an environment which differs from the one experienced by their parents and the ways in which ideas about child-rearing are likely to change in successive generations.

Since the products of group discussion will be wall displays for other pupils to examine, the desks or tables should be clustered in the middle of the room in order to provide unhindered access for viewing.

Objectives

- to examine the range of views held by pupils about how they see themselves behaving as parents
- to consider the consequences of their suggested behaviour upon the lives of their children

Materials

Large sheets of newsprint
Thick felt-tip pens
Pencils
Four blank cards (postcard size) for each pupil
Masking tape or blu-tak

Procedure

a Divide the class into groups of four. Give each group a sheet of newsprint and a felt-tip pen. At the top of the paper, one group member writes:
'If I were a parent, I would . . .'
Ask groups to suggest as many responses as possible to this sentence. All responses should be recorded without further analysis or comment, however unlikely or outrageous they may appear to be. (10 minutes)

b Each group displays its work on the wall. As pupils view the contributions, invite them to consider which statements may have a good effect and which may have a bad effect upon 'their' children. Pupils may wish to discuss the displays with their friends as they read the statements. (5 minutes)

c Give each pupil four plain postcards. Ask them to record *two* statements which are likely to have a good effect and *two* which may have a bad effect upon children in the family. The statements may be copied from the displays and/or created. (5–8 minutes)

d Each pupil returns to his original group of four. From the eight positive statements, the group is asked to identify the two which, if enacted within a family setting, may have the greatest positive effect upon the lives of the children. Explain that groups should negotiate the selection of the two cards and then consider how they may justify their selection to another group. (You may need to point out that just because a sentence appears on more than one card, the group need not automatically include it in the final selection.) (5–10 minutes)

e Ask groups to join up to form groups of eight and discuss their respective decisions. (10 minutes)

f Give the new groupings a clean sheet of newsprint and a felt pen. Invite them to devise a slogan based on the positive and negative cards, which will indicate the way in which they propose to behave towards their children. The slogans replace the earlier wall displays and may be used as a basis for the next activity, *Family carousel*.

Prompts for reflection

• A good parent is one who . . .
• Sometimes it is difficult for parents to . . .

- The most difficult thing about being a parent is . . .
- The best thing about being a parent is . . .

Suggestions for follow-up work

Ask pupils to collect headlines from magazines and newspapers, which refer to parents. The collection should be made over a period of several days/weeks. Pupils might also compose their own headlines. (All the contributions should reflect a positive view of parenting, rather than 'shock-horror' stories.)

Pupils could compile a scrapbook using the headlines, or devise a book of their own using captions, headlines and slogans as well as artwork and written contributions.

10.4 Family Carousel

Throughout life we are required to respond to situations where only limited preparation is possible. We are often asked questions that require immediate responses and there is no time to seek the advice of others or to refer to any other sources.

In this activity, pupils are asked four questions on family life in quick succession. This taxes their knowledge recall and learning from past experience as well as the ability to 'think on one's feet'. The questions provided (page 289) are examples and may be replaced by either pupil- or teacher-generated ones.

The exercise raises a number of issues; for example, how helpful is it to provide an unconsidered answer, particularly in circumstances where the questioner is likely to act immediately upon the advice or suggestion? How should we respond to someone who has a problem or is in crisis when they seek our opinion as a friend?

The carousel procedure may be used for other topics, where pupils devise their own questions. It can be adapted for revision purposes, for the reinforcement of earlier learning and as a way of ascertaining the knowledge limitations of pupils.

Objectives

- to examine a range of unprepared responses to the same question relating to family life

Materials

Eight *Question cards* (page 289) for each group of eight pupils

Procedure

a Divide the class into groups of eight. In each group four pupils sit back-to-back in a rectangular formation, facing outwards towards the classroom walls. The other four pupils in the group sit facing one of the 'inner' group (see Figure 10.b). Where the class number is not divisible by four, some pupils are paired in the inner rectangle (as in groups Y and Z, Figure 10.b).

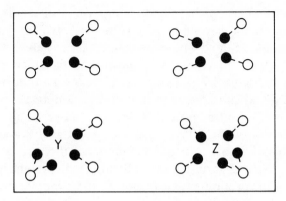

Fig. 10.b   Carousel arrangements for a class of 34 pupils

b Give each pupil on the outside rectangle one question card, (**A, B, C** or **D**). He asks the question of the person sitting opposite him on the inner rectangle (see Situation 1, Figure 10.c). It is important to emphasise that the questioner should seek as full an answer as possible.

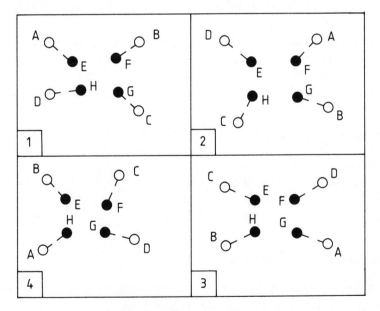

Fig. 10.c   Carousel arrangement in a group

When you feel groups have had enough time (in the first instance, 30 seconds to one minute may be sufficient), ask the pupils on the *outer* rectangle to move one place to their left.

c Pupils **A**, **B**, **C** and **D** ask their question to their new partner (see Situation 2, Figure 10.c). (You may increase the time available for this second and subsequent rounds of questioning.)

d The procedure continues until each of the 'outer' pupils have asked their question of the 'inner' ones (see Situations 3 and 4, Figure 10.c). It is advisable to use a maximum of three minutes for any question, bearing in mind the difficulty which some pupils may experience in sustaining their response. If any pupils feel unsure, it may help if you work alongside them.

e Pupils from different groups who have asked the same question discuss the range of responses they received *without mentioning the name of any respondent*. Pupils in the inner rectangle of each group seek to identify and discuss the most demanding question they were asked. (5–10 minutes)

f Invite comments from the holders of similar questions and from the respondent groups about their feelings while doing the exercise. (Maximum 10 minutes) The identification of issues for further work is likely to occur.

g Depending upon time, the questioner and respondent roles may be reversed so that pupils **E**, **F**, **G** and **H** become the 'outer' group and **A**, **B**, **C** and **D** take the inner position. The de-briefing session will follow as indicated in item **f** above.

Prompts for reflection

• When I am asked a difficult question I feel . . .
• Being able to answer a question makes me feel . . .
• If I do not know the answer to a question, I might go to . . .
• I think I know a lot about . . .

Suggestions for follow-up work

Invite the class to devise a set of questions so that the approach may be used in a different context; for example, how to
• prepare for examinations
• do homework
• behave in a range of social contexts . . .

Question cards

What help does a
working mother need
in the home?

What jobs in the home
should be done by
men?

If a woman is
expecting a baby, what
help does she need in
the home?

In what ways should
people of our age help
in and around the
home?

What things do
parents need to
provide for their
teenagers?

What are the good
things about belonging
to a large family?

What things do
parents need to
provide for their new-
born baby?

In what ways are boys
and girls treated
differently by their
parents?

1986   David Settle/Charles Wise   Basil Blackwell

10.5 Learning to share

Self-disclosure requires a trusting environment in which the individual feels safe to reveal what he feels. You should never lure pupils into a false sense of security where they subsequently regret their revelations or are exposed to the insensitivity of other class members. The notion that 'A problem shared is a problem halved' may in reality become '. . . a problem doubled'.

Pupils will need to move around the room while talking to each other, so the furniture should be placed against the walls.

Objectives

- to identify agencies, groups, individuals and organisations with whom one may or may not wish to share a particular problem
- to consider the issues raised by sharing a problem with one's peers

Materials

Pencils
One set of *Problem situations* (pages 292–293) and a *Learning to share* sheet (page 294) for each pupil

Procedure

a Begin by setting the scene, stressing the need for trust in this activity:
'We all face problems at various stages in our lives. We need other people's support and understanding to make us feel cared for and valued. If we need help we don't turn to just anyone, we choose people who we feel may be able to help and in whom we trust.'
b Give each person a copy of the 24 *Problem situations*. Explain that all these problems have been identified by 13-year-olds. Give each pupil a *Learning to share* sheet.
c As a private exercise, each pupil records the problem which interests him most and writes the *number* in the left-hand column of the *Learning to share* sheet, along with the problem as described on the card.

d The pupil then seeks to complete the remaining three columns with the names of people and agencies. (10 minutes)

e Invite pupils to circulate in the room in order to find one or two other people who have focused upon the same problem.

f Each newly-formed group sits around a table and members discuss their completed sheets on the common problem. Pupils who cannot find anyone who has focused on the same problem should form groups and discuss their respective responses.

g As a private task, each pupil writes down, in note form, any problems that he is prepared to share with other group members. He may wish to copy or amend one or more of the problems on the *Problem sheet*. There should not be any discussion at this stage. (5 minutes)

h Group members outline their problems and identify *one* problem which they all share. They write the details of the problem on their *Learning to share* sheet in the section 'We have the following problem'. You may need to help some groups clarify the nature of their chosen problem. (7–10 minutes)

i Each group focuses upon its problems and records its decision on one sheet.

Prompts for reflection

- I am prepared to share some problems with . . .
- The worst thing about sharing a problem with someone is . . .
- When I hear the word 'problem' it reminds me about . . .
- I would discuss *any* problem with . . .

Suggestions for follow-up work

1 Invite pupils to use the carousel method (see page 286) to look at some of the 24 statements in this activity. The pupil in possession of the statement reads it to his partner and asks 'What can I do?'

2 Some pupils could undertake action research to find which statutory and voluntary agencies in their local community provide support for young people who seek guidance or information relating to personal problems.

Problem situations

1 My parents will not let me have my friends in our house.	2 I think my mother may be very ill.
3 I don't have as much pocket money as my friends.	4 We live in a tiny house and there is not one quiet room in which I can do my homework.
5 I am no good at sport so nobody picks me for their team during PE lessons.	6 I want to be a brain surgeon but nobody takes me seriously.
7 I don't think I'm as well-developed as my friends.	8 I know someone who is on drugs but I don't know how to help without getting her into trouble.
9 Some older pupils are threatening to beat me up on the way home tonight.	10 I have lost interest in my school work.
11 I'm very clever and nobody will sit by me on the school bus.	12 My parents don't like the clothes I wear when I go out with friends.

Problem situations – continued

CHOICES

13 I know someone who steals money from his mother's purse every week.

14 Teachers like me a lot and people in my class call me 'teacher's pet'.

15 My friends try to force me to smoke.

16 I am upset because my grandmother died recently.

17 My parents still think of me as their 'little baby'.

18 My brother did well in his exams last year and my parents think I can do as well as him. I can't.

19 My parents are always arguing.

20 I have to look after my younger sisters when my parents go out for a drink three times a week.

21 Some pupils tease me about my hairstyle.

22 I find it difficult to talk to my father.

23 My family is not very rich.

24 I keep crying for no real reason.

Learning to share

CHOICES

Problem No	Problem	I *would* seek help from . . .	I *might* seek help from . . .	I would *not* seek help from . . .
	We share the following problem:	We *would* seek help from . . .	We *might* seek help from . . .	We would *not* seek help from . . .

10.6 Designed to help

Young people are often unaware of groups or individuals in the community who they could help. This activity may encourage pupils to think about their potential contribution to the well-being of others. (Examples of people who might benefit from this activity are given in *Suggestions for follow-up work.*)

In the activity, pupils are asked to produce a collage which shows the range of help and support needed by a chosen individual or group. Some time before the lesson, ask pupils to collect and bring in a range of suitable materials, to supplement those provided by the school. It is advisable to establish how many groups there will be, so that sufficient materials are available. An art room would be an ideal work centre for this activity.

The production of a collage involves a great deal of action, collaboration, negotiation and participation among group members. Not only must the design and presentation be discussed but, more importantly, the issues to be represented and the identification of appropriate materials and items form a major focus of the activity. Each group member is responsible for the outcome of this collective task. As a result, some groups may wish to take further action and provide support for the individual or group which is the subject of its collage.

You may well find that one lesson is not long enough for the activity, and groups will need to continue their work in the next session.

Objectives

- to identify groups or individuals who may benefit from the help provided by pupils in the class
- to identify the needs of a specific group or individual

Materials

For each group

Brushes	Paste and glue
Coloured card (offcuts)	Plain scrap paper
Colour magazines	Scissors

Fabrics	Sheets of newsprint
Felt pens	String
Large sheets of sugar paper	Tinfoil
Mail order catalogue	Wool
Newspapers	Paints

(Parents and pupils may be able to supply some materials.)

Procedure

a Invite the class to brainstorm suggestions as to individuals and groups which they could help. At this stage, the nature and scope of the help does not have to be stated. People of any age and in any location may be identified; there are no barriers to the inclusion of particular groups. Record all suggestions on the blackboard or on a large sheet of newsprint. (3–5 minutes)

b Ask pupils to form self-selected groups. Each group sits at a table which contains a bank of materials.

c Each group selects one named individual or group from the list whom it would *ideally* like to help. (4 minutes)

d Explain that each group will use the materials to produce a collage which shows the range of help and support it believes to be necessary.

e Point out, either verbally or on the blackboard, that groups should first:
  • identify the nature and scope of help to be represented;
  • examine the materials available and consider their potential;
  • explore the design possibilities in rough draft;
  • decide upon a division of labour that accommodates the abilities of all pupils in the group

f In addition to its attraction as a wall display, the collage may stimulate discussion as to how individuals or the group may *take action* to provide help and support; their response may be generated from their own or another group's collage.

Prompts for reflection

• At the moment, my top priority for helping others is . . .
• When I help someone, I feel . . .
• Throughout my life, I will always help . . .
• Sometimes I don't help people because . . .
• To help someone means . . .

Suggestions for follow-up work

1 Invite pupils to compose a 30-second tape-recorded message which aims to raise the awareness of pupils throughout the school about the needs of a specific group within the community for example, elderly people, pre-school children, a community group, charity organisations or people in hospital . . .

It may be possible to interest the staff of your local radio station in the project and to seek their advice on how best to promote a particular cause.

2 Pupils could design a logo which would be appropriate for the cover of an information pack relating to the tape produced in item 1.

3 Encourage pupils to use an action-research approach to enquire into the needs of a named individual or group, and to ascertain how these needs could be met.

10.7 Good things

This activity emphasises the positive experiences of human life, and as such may seem misplaced in a chapter which focuses upon 'problems'. However, to ensure that neither the reader nor the pupils view young people only in terms of problems, we offer here a forum for the expression of positive feelings. After earlier lessons, which examined conflict and disagreement, this activity provides a situation where ten positive aspects of sexuality may be considered. The onset of puberty does not represent a single, specific event, it is a stage in the development of a person towards adulthood. While each sex may have different ideas as to what constitutes 'good things', it is likely that they will also share similar pleasurable feelings about growing up.

In the activity, pupils discuss the perceptions of boys and girls relating to members of the opposite sex, and produce a set of cards stating these ideas. (You may need to remind pupils that their written materials should not contain expressions which are likely to cause offence.) Boys and girls work in separate groups to generate resource materials. This segregation increases the effectiveness of the activity.

Encouraging pupils to use their experience and expertise to create their own resources has a number of advantages:

- pupils are learning during the process of creating materials
- pupils take 'ownership' of their materials and may show greater commitment when they are used among peers
- materials produced by the teacher may not accurately reflect the perceptions of young people on a particular issue
- involving pupils in the creation of materials will save the teacher considerable time and energy.

It is possible to use this activity in a single-sex setting, but one group will obviously have to offer the perspective of members of the opposite sex.

Objectives

- to share perceptions of the good features of being male or female

Materials

20–24 blank cards for each group
Pencils

Procedure

a Divide the class into single-sex groups of between three and six members. *There should be an equal number of male and female groups.*

b Give each group a set of 10–12 blank cards. Explain that the groups should discuss what they think are the good features of being a *girl*, and then write one of their ideas on each card. The group may decide to elect one 'scribe', or each group member may take responsibility for the completion of a number of cards. As each card is completed, the letter **G** should be written on the reverse.

c Give out a fresh set of cards. On these, groups write what they think are the good features of being a *boy*. As each card is completed, the letter **B** is recorded on the reverse. (20–25 minutes)

d Each group of boys joins a group of girls. Both groups retain their own cards. Invite groups to distribute the cards relating to boys equally among their own members. (Girls cards will be used later.) Alternatively, girls and boys take turns to read out a statement to the whole group until all the cards have been used.

e The whole group discusses which cards held by boys and girls offer similar views. These are placed on the table or floor in the middle of the group. Cards which contain contrasting views about the good features of being a boy are retained. (5 minutes)

f The group talks about these unique cards. If all cards have been shed, members may wish to consider some additional statements which indicate compatible or conflicting views. (10 minutes)

g The procedure is repeated and the 'Girls' cards are considered in a similar way. (It may be necessary to consider these cards during the next lesson if time is short.)

Prompts for reflection

• As a boy, I was surprised that girls think that . . .
• As a girl, I was surprised that boys think that . . .
• The greatest similarity between boys and girls is . . .
• Boys and girls think the same about . . .
• Working in mixed groups is . . .

Suggestions for follow-up work

1 Invite the class to collect advertisements where good features of being male or female are emphasised. The work may develop into a consideration of the roles of men and women in society and the way in which image-makers project sex stereotypes.
2 Using collage some pupils could create a view of the world where men and women enjoy equal rights.

10.8 Is this me?

In this activity, pupils are invited to reflect upon their ability to deal with their own problems and those presented by their peers. Through a self-perception exercise, each pupil assesses his strengths and weaknesses. As an extension, each pupil is asked to complete an identical form, this time as if he were another named person in the class. The purpose of this task is to try to anticipate how another person might complete the form. Identifying similarities and differences in 'the way I see myself' and 'how others see me' if handled sympathetically, may greatly assist pupils with their self-presentation.

Emphasising positive personal qualities is likely to enhance self-esteem; focusing on the negative aspects of a person through a direct attack, innuendo or 'put down' is likely to destroy self-confidence, particularly if repeated over a period of time.

The format of the proforma may be adapted for a range of other purposes, for example, course evaluation and the analysis of personal strengths and weaknesses relating to the achievement of a specific task. (For further examples of self-perception exercises, see Chapter 3 *Who am I?*)

Objectives

- to reflect upon how we deal with our own problems and those of others in need of help and support
- to listen to other pupils and interpret their responses

Materials

One *Listen carefully* form (page 303) for each pupil
One *Standing in someone else's shoes* form (page 304) for each pupil
Pencils

Procedure

a Give each pupil a copy of the *Listen carefully* form. Invite them to complete the form as a private task. (3–4 minutes)

b Ask each person to join with one or two others and to discuss their responses. Explain that there are four ground rules for this phase:
1 at no stage should a person's paper be given or shown to another group member. Any information relating to a statement must be conveyed verbally;
2 nobody is allowed to ask in which box another member placed a tick;
3 where pupils make short responses, group members should help them to offer a fuller explanation;
4 a group may start at any of the statements and proceed in any order until all responses have been considered.

These ground rules may be recorded on the blackboard or a sheet of newsprint, for pupils to refer to. (15–25 minutes)

c Ask pupils to complete the *Standing in someone else's shoes* form on behalf of their partner or one other group member. Read out four numbers and ask pupils for each of the corresponding statements to complete the proforma as they believe the subject did. (5 minutes)

d Pupils give the completed form to their partners. As a group, members discuss the similarities and differences in their own views and those of the person who was trying 'to stand in their shoes'.

Prompts for reflection

• I was surprised to hear that . . .
• If I had listened more carefully, I . . .
• Listening is . . .
• I think I am a caring person because . . .
• If I am faced with a difficult problem, I . . .

Suggestions for follow-up work

1 Invite the group to devise games which seek to assess people's ability to listen.
2 In small groups, ask pupils to design a procedure for evaluating a course or lesson using the same format. In discussing items to be included, the pupils will inevitably consider their evaluative criteria. Groups may wish to change the headings of the respective columns.

Listen carefully

CHOICES

Do not write your name on this paper.

You will *not* be asked to show your responses to anyone else, but you will use them for discussion with a partner(s) of your own choice.

Place a tick (√) in *one* of the four boxes alongside each statement.

Be honest. Read each statement carefully.

		Always	Often	Sometimes	Never
1	I am willing to help people with their problems	☐	☐	☐	☐
2	I think people should discuss their problems with friends	☐	☐	☐	☐
3	I discuss my problems with adults	☐	☐	☐	☐
4	I think people trust me	☐	☐	☐	☐
5	People ask for my advice	☐	☐	☐	☐
6	I think I understand what upsets other people of my age	☐	☐	☐	☐
7	I avoid having arguments with friends	☐	☐	☐	☐
8	I am able to make unhappy people feel better	☐	☐	☐	☐
9	I need close friends	☐	☐	☐	☐

© 1986   David Settle/Charles Wise   Basil Blackwell

Standing in someone else's shoes

CHOICES

This is how I think _____ completed his/her form.

I will show him my responses.

Only complete numbers . . . .

	Always	Often	Sometimes	Never
1 I am willing to help people with their problems	☐	☐	☐	☐
2 I think people should discuss their problems with friends	☐	☐	☐	☐
3 I discuss my problems with adults	☐	☐	☐	☐
4 I think people trust me	☐	☐	☐	☐
5 People ask for my advice	☐	☐	☐	☐
6 I think I understand what upsets other people of my age	☐	☐	☐	☐
7 I avoid having arguments with friends	☐	☐	☐	☐
8 I am able to make unhappy people feel better	☐	☐	☐	☐
9 I need close friends	☐	☐	☐	☐

11 Helping each other

If we are asked to conjure up a picture of helping others we may well be tempted to go for an accepted image – to which we are invited to aspire. Florence Nightingale tending the wounded at Scutari, Albert Schweitzer devoting his life to the sick at Lambarene, Laurence Oates walking off into the Antarctic blizzard . . . These images of heroism are extreme examples of help given to others. The stories of such people form part of a framework of second-hand experience on which young people are invited to construct a view of positive human characteristics and qualities. Without denying the part that this experience can play it seems foolish to rely on this when young people themselves are surrounded by their own first-hand experiences of helping. Help is often seen in concrete terms: doing the shopping for Dad, cutting Grandma's lawn, cleaning out the budgerigar's cage. But in focusing on such tasks we may lose sight of the fact that help can be given and received in many other ways.

One of the most significant forms of help we can give to others is our time, especially if it is time to listen. Listening with sensitivity signals to the speaker that the things they have to say, and they themselves, really matter. When help in this form is associated with caring, supporting and trusting it becomes special, it binds together those involved in the helping process.

In a similar way helping others in a group setting can be an important experience. When groups take on tasks and work as a team, with mutual support, their achievements promote the formation of strong bonds between members. In this setting success is not always essential, failure can provide an equally binding force as members help each other to cope with and learn from it.

The activities in this chapter are based on the premise that an individual's natural tendency is to be helpful. We believe that this quality can be fostered within individuals and groups if opportunities for demonstrating trust, support and care are provided.

The eight activities can be used as a developmental sequence, culminating in the activity *Giving and receiving personal gifts* where group members symbolically present gifts to each other.

The *Group trust activities* and *Blind search* represent ways of developing trust within a group through concrete experience of trusting. As such they form an integral part of this sequence, but they can also be used with any other work that requires trust between pupils. In a group that will have a fixed membership for many months these kinds of activity should form part of an initial group building experience.

Succeeding in pairs and *Support builder* are designed to form a sequence of increasing difficulty of tasks, for pairs and then a larger group to work at. As well as being good fun they each provide achievable goals whereby individuals can experience giving and receiving help.

Teach-in offers an opportunity for everyone to demonstrate something they know or can do. The activity demonstrates that all of us have a capacity for helping others through our knowledge and skills. This leads on to the *Group problem solving* activity which represents a generic way of dealing with issues or problems that may arise in the group; it relies upon everyone helping everyone else.

11.1 Group trust activities

Abstract concepts such as trust are difficult to handle with groups of young people. It is seldom enough to introduce this important aspect of group work through personal adult anecdotes or by relying upon the young people themselves to come up with descriptions of situations in which they gave or received trust. What is needed is first-hand, concrete experience of trusting which will create not only a greater awareness of the meaning of trust but a growth of trust within the group.

Objectives

- to provide concrete experience of giving and receiving trust in a group

Materials

None

Procedure

A variety of trust games can be used with groups of young people. Many are fundamental to the active work of tutorial time as a developmental part of the pastoral curriculum. The following list is drawn in part from *Group Tutoring for the Form Teacher* by Leslie Button; *Active Tutorial Work* by Lancashire County Council; and *Gamesters' Handbook* by Donna Brandes.

BLIND TRUST

Working in pairs, pupils decide who is **A** and who is **B**. **B** takes the role of a blind person, **A** takes responsibility for leading him carefully around the room, describing the surroundings and bringing him into contact with the environment through sound and touch. The experience is repeated with the roles reversed.

Prompts for reflection

- The role I found most difficult was . . .
- When I was leading I found that . . .
- As the blind person I . . .

ROCKING IN PAIRS

Pupils decide who is **A** and **B**. **A** stands balanced with feet comfortably apart and with eyes closed. **B** stands behind **A**, weight spread evenly, poised to support the weight of **A**. **A** is invited to lean back slowly, putting his trust in **B** to support him. At first the angle of recline should only be slight, but it can be gradually increased, according to the limits of **B**'s capacity to support **A**'s weight.

A further development of the above is ROCKING IN THREES. This includes a forward rocking motion, where person **A** is held by **C**, who pushes him back to the vertical before he leans backwards to **B** again.

Both the activities should be repeated to give everyone the opportunity to experience the different positions.

Prompts for reflection

- During that activity, when I was being held I felt . . .
- When I was holding my partner I felt . . .

GROUP SUPPORT

Here groups of six or seven work together. One person stands in the centre of a circle made from the remainder of the group. All members of the circle hold the shoulders of the centre person, with their arms outstretched. The centre person stands with feet together, ready to be gently rocked and swayed by the other members of the group, as a demonstration of their capacity to support the individual.

GROUP LIFT continues from this point. The person in the centre leans back against one member of the circle and all the others take his body-weight to lift him to a horizontal position, meanwhile maintaining a gentle rocking motion. Finally, they slowly lower the individual to the ground.

Prompts for reflection

- During that activity I felt . . .
- As I was being lifted I felt . . .
- When I finally touched the ground I . . .

All the above activities have been used with groups over many years. They provide experiences of giving and receiving trust and opportunities for individuals to describe their personal perceptions of trusting. They give all people access to feelings common in the group; in so doing they heighten their awareness of the needs of others and promote care, sensitivity and support within the group.

It is very important that you have direct personal experience of these activities. Without this you may find it difficult to match your comments to the feelings developed within the pupils. You should also be ready to participate with the pupils in these activities; if the generation of a support group is a major objective of this work, it will necessitate you being available as a group member on equal terms. Where teachers have been willing to receive the full trust and support (*physical* support) of their pupils, the depth of relationship within the whole group has often visibly moved forwards.

Suggestions for follow-up work

Many more activities for trust building can be found in the books listed at the back of this book.

11.2 Blind search

There are very few occasions when a whole class can demonstrate care for its members. Often these occasions are restricted to the times when individuals are ill and absent over a prolonged period.

The purpose of this activity is to create an atmosphere of support and trust within the class by allowing the whole group to demonstrate its capacity to care for an individual within a well-defined set of circumstances.

The activity is a variation of the well-known game 'Blind Man's Buff'. Here, however, rather than simply 'groping in the dark', the blindfolded player is guided by the rest of the group until he encounters a chosen group member.

After each attempt it is helpful if the class discusses how they can best help the searcher and/or the searcher's guide. The purpose is to be as supportive as possible and the quality of communication is a key to success.

Objectives

- to promote group trust and support
- to provide experience of group trust and support for individuals
- to give a group access to the feeling of success based upon cooperation

Materials

A large space is needed for this activity – a hall or gymnasium is ideal though a large classroom is acceptable

Procedure

a Arrange a number of desks or chairs in the centre of the open space to act as obstacles.
b Invite the class to form a large circle around the perimeter of the room.

c Ask for one person to volunteer to be blindfolded and stand alone in the middle of the circle.

d The group decides silently who will be the person *to be sought*.

e The object is for the group to guide the blind searcher to his destination by spoken directions, without any other contacts being made. The class must decide how they are going to cooperate in order to achieve this.

f Allow a number of volunteers to experience this activity as the blindfolded person.

g Debrief the exercise using the prompts provided below.

h Invite two people to leave the room, one to be blindfolded, the other to act as his guide.

i The rest of the class decide who is to be sought then arrange themselves at random throughout the room, some in clusters, others individually.

j The blindfolded searcher is led back into the room by his guide, who is now the only person allowed to speak.

k Using only non-verbal signs from the class the guide gives spoken instructions to the searcher in an attempt to direct him/her to the person to be sought.

Prompts for reflection

- As the blind person in that exercise I . . .
- As a group member in that exercise I . . .
- The most difficult part of that exercise was . . .
- What I liked most about that was . . .

Suggestions for follow-up work

Repeat either procedure but have two blind people at one time, thereby giving the group an added responsibility for more effective communications.

11.3 Succeeding in pairs

This activity provides enormous scope for personal achievement and support in pairs. It is a developmental sequence designed to allow all participants to taste success. It is non-competitive and entirely cooperative. The emphasis is on the use of language as a basis of clear and precise instructions to assist a partner in completing a task. It also requires good listening skills.

There are three stages in the activity, although each can be used in isolation. Taken together the stages form a sequence of increasing difficulty, and you may need to consider whether the group is ready to tackle each stage successfully.

Since this activity involves a precise vocabulary you may well wish to make vocabulary development the key learning aim. The activity can function equally well in a second language or mother tongue, in which case a simple vocabulary of terms must first be developed.

Objectives

• to heighten the effectiveness and accuracy of spoken instructions
• to heighten awareness of the need for effective listening

Materials

Sufficient 8-stud Lego bricks to allow 10 bricks for each pupil
A number of simple line drawings (see *Succeeding in pairs sheet* on page 314)
A set of more complex drawings or photographs with a common theme, eg cars, buildings, people . . . (pages from catalogues or magazines are ideal)
Pieces of A4 paper – attached to clipboards or with something to rest on
Pencils

Procedure

a Invite the class to work in pairs and decide who is **A** and **B**.
b **A** and **B** sit back-to-back and agree not to look over their shoulders but to communicate only by speaking.

c **A** makes a shape using the ten Lego bricks provided.
d **B** attempts to make the same shape, under instruction from **A**. When the construction is finished the original and the copy are compared.
e **A** and **B** exchange roles and repeat the procedure. (It is quite possible that pupils will wish to repeat the activity several times.)
f Invite pupils to discuss the activity, using prompts such as:
  • The most difficult role for me was . . .
  • The most frustrating part of that was . . .
  • At the end, when we put the two shapes together, I . . .
g Repeat the procedure, this time replacing the Lego bricks with a simple line drawing for **A** and a piece of paper and pencil for **B**.
h **A** describes as accurately as possible the size and nature of the drawing, and **B** attempts to reproduce it.
i Invite pairs to exchange roles and give them a new set of materials.
j Further attempts could involve pictures of more complex subjects – vehicles, animals, people, an arrangement of objects etc.

Prompts for reflection

• The most interesting task of the three was . . .
• The part which gave me most difficulty was . . .
• I would say my listening skills are . . .
• One thing I have learnt from this activity is . . .

Suggestions for follow-up work

1 Develop the idea of working in mother tongue. With pupils, establish a basic vocabulary of terms for such words as on, under, left, right etc. Then introduce the activities to see who can listen and recall the basic vocabulary.
2 Instead of sitting back-to-back invite pupils to sit facing each other and communicate non-verbally.

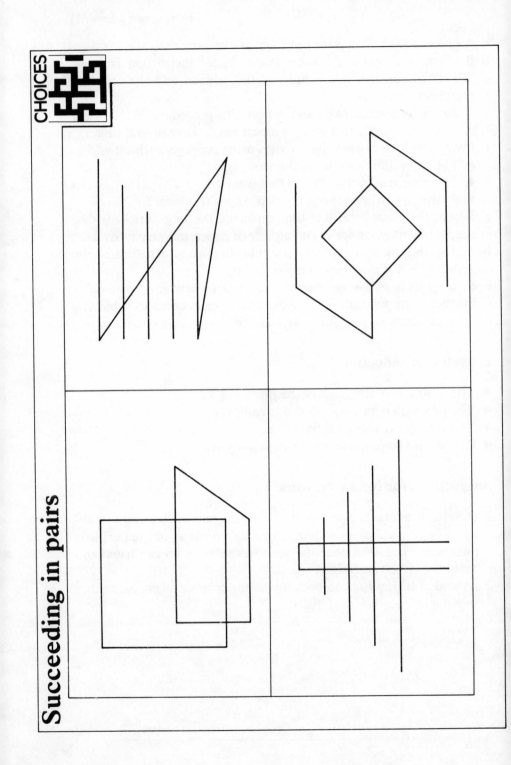

Succeeding in pairs

CHOICES

11.4 Support builder

This activity is an extension of the previous activity *Succeeding in pairs*. It develops the notion of support and extends the need for cooperation within a larger group. The task is more complex and requires considerable planning and leadership if a group is to be successful.

The inclusion of an observer introduces another dimension of support and cooperation. It also offers a new role for an individual to fulfil on behalf of the group.

Objectives

- to provide an opportunity for team work
- to provide a difficult task with a tangible outcome

Materials

For each group Half a box of drinking straws, 2 metres of string, a pair of scissors, one glass marble and a ball of Blu-tak of equal size to the marble, 3 small elastic bands, 5 pieces of A4 paper, a pencil.
One *Instruction card* (page 317)
One *Role checker chart* (page 318)

Procedure

a Invite the class to form groups of five or six.
b Each group elects an observer who will report back on the quality of team work at the end of the task.
c Give each group a set of materials and an *Instruction card*.
d Explain that the purpose of the activity is to work as a team to achieve a task. The observer in each group should watch closely and note down his observations on the *Role checker chart* as the group works on the task. This information will later be fed back to the group.
e Invite the group to read the *Instruction card* carefully and then use the materials to carry out the task. They have 30 minutes to build the structure.

Prompts for reflection

- We decided who would do what by . . .
- The bit that I contributed to the end result was . . .
- The thing that I am most pleased with is . . .
- As the observer, I noticed that . . .
- During the activity I felt . . .
- When time was up I . . .

Suggestions for follow-up work

Many similar construction tasks can be created at minimal cost. They always offer a challenge to young people's imagination and ingenuity. They also provide opportunities for individuals to take specific roles; these can be reflected on by the group in order to raise their awareness of their own needs and the needs of others. Fulfilling the task is not the end, merely a means to an end.

Instruction card

The purpose of this activity is to build a
structure capable of holding a glass marble
above the ground. The structure should be as
high as possible and self supporting. There
should be an observer to note the particular
roles that people take and record these on the
role checker chart provided.

At the end of 30 minutes you can compare
your result with those of other groups after
which your observer should tell you about the
way you worked together.

Check your materials carefully

30 drinking straws	1 piece of Blu-tak
2 metres of string	3 small elastic bands
1 pair of scissors	5 × A4 pieces of paper
1 glass marble	1 pencil

) 1986   David Settle/Charles Wise   Basil Blackwell

CHOICES

Role checker chart

roles \ names					
drew plans					
made suggestions					
argued					
kept group active					
built the structure					
kept silent					
others					

11.5 Teach-in

Most pupils have some specialist or personal knowledge which no-one else in the group possesses. This activity uses that fact and builds on it as a way of demonstrating that this knowledge *can* be made available to others. The onus is on those who do not know to find out from the person with the knowledge, not the other way around. The suggested whole class demonstration allows you to make clear the need for precise and direct questioning.

This way of working demonstrates one way in which pupils can help each other but it also represents a fundamental skill which needs to be developed in all pupils – the ability to think through the questions that should be asked in order to acquire the information required.

Objectives

- to demonstrate that everyone has some knowledge or skill to offer others
- to develop the skill of direct questioning

Materials

None

Procedure

a Invite the class to arrange themselves in a circle or, if space is limited, to cluster at one end of the room.

b Ask everyone to think of something that they know quite a lot about or a particular skill that they have.

c Ask for a volunteer who will help you demonstrate how the class will work in this activity.

d Ask the volunteer to come to the centre of the circle or the front of the group. Invite two others to join him and join them yourself.

e Invite the volunteer to describe the thing that he knows so much about, or the particular skill he has.

f Demonstrate the skill of direct questioning by establishing first of all precisely what it is that the person knows, then find out more by asking open-ended questions.

g Invite the other two to join in the questioning.

h After more detail has come out, pause to explain more fully the use of open questions. Demonstrate by asking a number of people very pointed closed questions – then use examples of open ones.

i Invite the whole class to form threes. In groups, members take it in turns to have three minutes each questioning one person at a time.

j Combine groups of three to make sixes. Invite everyone to have a turn at explaining to the new partners as much as they can of what they have learned from one of the original partners.

Prompts for reflection

● For me the hardest part of this has been . . .
● When I was being questioned I felt . . .
● When I was questioning someone else I . . .
● When I had to tell other people what I had learned I . . .
● I could use this idea again when . . .

Suggestions for follow-up work

1 Invite groups to use the same strategy to find out specialist knowledge from adults, for example in questioning grandparents for historical facts.

2 Small groups could use the same procedure as a means of peer- and self-assessment, within the overall context of assessing factual recall and the ability to explain information succinctly.

11.6 Group problem solving

Very often groups of pupils find themselves with a common problem. Perhaps a decision has to be made about an outing, a visit, or a school holiday. On the other hand, the problem may be concerned with the class getting a bad name. The possible bases for identifying a whole class issue are enormous.

The approach used in this activity is a generic problem-solving technique which can be used either by individuals or groups; it particularly lends itself to work which requires support in groups. As such it is transferable into all kinds of situations.

Objectives

- to establish a system of problem solving for the group
- to identify a situation seen by the group to be a problem

Materials

Large piece of newsprint, flip chart sheet or blackboard

Procedure

a Invite the class to describe a problem or situation that faces all of them and which requires all of them to be involved. If no current 'problem' exists within the group, then issues such as future examinations, homework, revision etc can be used.
b Invite the class to identify and describe clearly what the 'problem' is. (It may be necessary to give help with the language if pupils have real difficulties.)
c Ensure that everyone accepts that it is *their* problem, that they own it, and invite the class to brainstorm as many solutions as possible to the problem.
d In small groups invite the pupils to decide on the best solutions offered in the brainstorm.
e Invite the groups to vote on the solutions offered in order to identify the one idea agreed by the majority in the class to be the best solution.

f Pupils return to their small groups and list things that will get in the way of the solution being successful (hinderances) and things that will help to make the solution successful (helping factors).

g Pool the lists from the small groups and keep them to check their accuracy.

h Explain that the class should agree to abide by the chosen solution to the identified problem and to put it to the test for a fixed period of time. (1 or 2 weeks)

i Invite the class to decide on a future date when the chosen solution will be judged in the light of experience.

Prompts for reflection

• My feeling about the chosen problem is . . .
• My feelings about the chosen solution are . . .
• I could use this approach to problem solving in my . . .
• The part of this lesson I liked least was . . .
• What I liked most about the lesson was . . .

Suggestions for follow-up work

Invite the pupils to identify something in their friendship groups that needs attention and to which they are willing to apply the problem-solving strategy.

11.7 Help I have given and received

It is possible to go through life without being aware of the part other people play in our lives and we in theirs. In particular it is easy to miss opportunities for giving help to others and to fail to recognise when help is being given.

This activity invites young people to reflect on their own lives and the help they have given and received. It is not an attempt to invite judgements about the quality or nature of help. It aims merely to draw attention to the place that giving and receiving help plays in our lives.

Objectives

- to sensitise pupils to the help they give and receive
- to help pupils to identify help they would like to have

Materials

A *Helpers checklist* and pencil for each pair

Procedure

a Invite the class to divide up into pairs.
b Give out the *Helpers checklists*.
c Explain that pupils will work closely in their pairs in order to identify help they have given and received in each of the categories listed on the sheet.
d Invite the pairs to check if there is someone each person needs to thank for help they have been given without really realising it.
e Ask the partners to contract with each other to thank the people they have identified.
f Invite the pairs to use the prompts for reflection.

Prompts for reflection

- The most important help I have received is . . .
- The help I most enjoyed giving was . . .

- The help I would like to receive but haven't is . . .
- The help I would like to give you is . . .
- The person I must thank for their help today is . . .

Suggestions for follow-up work

1 Invite pupils to use the same approach to do an analysis of local helping agencies.
2 Groups could combine the activity with a plan to contact a group of elderly people in the local community.

CHOICES

Helpers checklist

categories	help received	help given
school		
home		
friends		
adults		
clubs/teams		
younger people		

11.8 Giving and receiving personal gifts

The giving and receiving of gifts is something that gives most people pleasure. Birthdays and special feast days tend to be the main occasions although in friendship groups giving and receiving – seen as sharing – is a common practice. Gifts symbolically represent the bond of care between people; the time and trouble taken to think and act for another.

This activity provides pupils with an opportunity to demonstrate their capacity to care by offering each other symbolic 'gifts' in the form of statements based upon what they know their friends would like to have.

Objectives

- to demonstrate care in a group by giving supportive statements
- to reflect on personal knowledge of the needs of others

Materials

Enough small pieces of paper to provide a minimum of five per person

Procedure

a Invite the class to form groups of four – on the basis of having worked together.
b Display prompt stem phrases (below) based on the work over the previous few weeks on the topic *Helping Each Other*.
  - When we worked together on . . . I . . .
  - I was most happy when we were working on . . .
  - The activity I liked least was . . .
  - What I learned about each of you is . . .
  - What I learned about myself is . . .
  Ask groups to use these as a basis for conversation.
c Invite the fours to sit in silence for a minute thinking about what they have learned about each other.

d Ask each person to list the names of those people they have worked with. Each name should then be written on to a single small piece of paper.

e Invite each person to think of a symbolic 'gift' they would like to give to each named person – something they think that person would value. The gifts are written on the slip of paper bearing the recipient's name.

f Invite the group to stand together in the centre of the room and then to move around, giving out their gifts.

g When all the 'gifts' are given out, invite the group to read them in private and to discuss them with others if they would like to.

h Ask the class to return to their groups to use the following prompts for reflection.

Prompts for reflection

- The gift I most enjoyed giving was . . .
- The gift I most enjoyed receiving was . . .
- The part I like best about giving or receiving gifts is . . .
- If I could have anything in the world I would have . . .

Suggestions for follow-up work

The idea of giving gifts could be extended to a wider friendship group or, if appropriate, to the whole class or the family.

12 Looking forward

The future remains unknown; we have faith that tomorrow will come – things might even get better! But we can claim little more for the future. This lack of certainty makes some people feel fearful, insecure and pessimistic, while others feel confident, excited and optimistic. Perhaps it is most appropriate to suggest that there are some aspects of the future and our lives over which we may exert greater control than others. In this final section, *Looking forward*, we aim to engender a spirit of hope in young people, hope which emanates from the realisation that an individual *does* possess personal power to act independently and in concert with others.

For the school leaver, the world of paid employment has changed considerably during the past decade, with the growth of youth unemployment and the introduction of government-sponsored training schemes. The idea of having one career for life seems, for many, a distant reminder of the past. With rapid social and technological change, long-term planning and projection may appear purely speculative.

In this chapter we provide activities which highlight the unknown but which suggest that the young person *does* have the potential to influence the course of some events in his life. The inevitability of the ageing process for all of us also features in the work.

The opening activity, *Towards a better future*, sets the tone of optimism and self-empowerment which we would wish young people to develop. It does not provide a falsely rosy scenario, but rather offers young people the opportunity to create their own vision of the future. Through the production of attractive visual material which will be displayed, the classroom may be transformed so that pupils look forward rather than backward. Wall displays are a regular feature in primary schools and we believe that they also have the potential to enhance the learning of young people in the secondary school.

From the macro-level of tomorrow's world *A perfect day* looks at one snapshot within this context, a situation where happiness abounds. All pupils face the prospect of leaving school sometime after the age of 16. This event and the following 12 months are the subject of *Certainty*. Pupils are invited to complete the sentence stem 'When I leave school I will . . . ' and categorise their statements under the headings of *maybe, almost certain* and *certain*. They then have the opportunity to discuss their views with each other and to cite a range of personal circumstances.

In *Double your age* the pupil takes a further 'step' into the future and extends his view of himself to his own village, town or city, and to his country. The 21st century is rapidly approaching, so in *Predictions* we focus on the year 2001. Pupils are asked to predict what events might have occurred by this year and to indicate the likelihood of their occurrence. The activity's primary function is to encourage the presentation of reasoned argument, based on pupils' existing knowledge; no time is provided for reference to other sources.

The best-laid plans may be upset by unpredictable events and in *Life chances* pupils consider a number of situations which punctuate someone's happy life.

Our ambitions and aspirations tend to influence our view of the future and there are times when we welcome the opportunity to share our thoughts with a friend. In *High hopes* pupils exchange views on how they see their early years of adulthood. The activity requires each person to listen carefully to his partner so that he can (with the permission of the partner) describe what he has heard to another pair.

In *Success story* pupils look back on their lives from the perspective of their 70th birthday. The task is a complex one, demanding that pupils first project themselves forward to that age, and then reflect upon significant events along the way. This is probably the most demanding exercise in the book, but it is a rewarding and stimulating experience.

One day, today's young people may be mothers and fathers. In the final section *For our next generation* they consider what messages about their schooling experience they wish to convey to their own children.

12.1 Towards a better future

This activity involves the production of collages which will help to create a stimulating environment in which work related to the future will take place. It also encourages young people to view the future with optimism as the themes offered point towards a better future.

It is helpful to establish groupings some time before the lesson, so that pupils can begin to collect their own materials. Local firms and organisations may be willing to contribute small quantities of junk and packing materials, offcuts and surplus stock. Although the list of suggested materials is extensive, many items may be readily available in the home or the work place.

So that each person is able to make a contribution, pupils should work in pairs or groups of three. The more groups there are, the greater will be the number of displays and the potential visual impact. Large groups also tend to work more slowly than small groups since there will be complex negotiations about the division of labour and the decision-making process.

If there is a limited amount of materials, you may need to create one central bank, but it is preferable to give each small group its own resources, even if this means limiting the range or quantity available.

Objectives

● to create a focus for work relating to the future

Materials

For each group – some of the following:

Brushes	Paints
Coloured card (offcuts)	Paste and glue
Colour magazines	Photographs from numerous sources
Coloured pencils	Plain scrap paper
Crepe paper	Polystyrene
Fabrics	Scissors
Felt-tip pens	Sheets of newsprint
Large sheets of sugar paper	String
Mail order catalogues	Tin foil
Newspapers	Wool

Procedure

a Ask pupils to form self-selected pairs or threes, and provide them with a bank of materials.

b Explain that groups will create a cartoon, collage or montage to illustrate one of the following captions:
  - 'It's a great life'
  - 'My ideal world'
  - 'The best job in the world'
  - 'No more trouble'
  - 'Happiness is . . . '
  If pupils wish to offer alternative captions under the general theme *Towards a better future*, these should be considered.

c Groups negotiate which caption they wish to work on, and make rough drafts of their ideas. (The activity may need more than one lesson and pupils may wish to continue their work after school hours.)

d Before pupils start work on their display material, negotiate a deadline for completion. You should consider how groups who finish ahead of time will be accommodated; they could
  - produce a display based on another caption
  - collect or produce supporting materials in another medium, eg music, poetry and prose
  - assist other groups
  - observe other groups

e Place the displays around the walls. They should remain in place for the duration of this unit, as the work is likely to provide a stimulus for other related activities.

Prompts for reflection

- Wall displays are useful because . . .
- The best thing about working as a group is . . .
- As a group, we found it difficult to . . .
- It is important to share our work with the class because . . .
- I think our display is . . .

Suggestions for follow-up work

1 This activity serves as a 'scene-setter' for all those which follow.

2 Pupils could develop the display for the school entrance or as support for an assembly or parents' evening.

12.2   A perfect day

In this activity, we invite pupils into a world of fantasy in which, on one day, everything goes right. A day on which all personal grief and sorrow is set aside, there are no limits to one's happiness and other people share the pleasurable experience. For some pupils, this fantasy may be completely at odds with their daily experience whereas for others, it may not be that far from reality.

If pupils have recently experienced personal loss – say, of a friend, pet, relative – it may be helpful for you to work alongside them as the activity may induce tears and upset. Helping young people cope with sadness and stress is, in the long run, kinder than suggesting that it can be eradicated.

During the final phase of the activity, the group considers whether or not it might be feasible to enact the 'perfect day' at some future date. Perhaps with minor adjustments the fantasy may become a reality and a classroom activity translated into a broader social context.

Objectives

- to explore ideals about what constitutes 'a perfect day'
- for peers to negotiate with each other as to how they could spend a perfect day together

Materials

Writing paper and a pencil for each pupil

Procedure

a Provide each pupil with a piece of writing paper and a pencil. Ask him to write, in annotated form, up to ten features of 'a perfect day'. The writer should not just focus upon one setting, for example, home, school or youth club, but should view the whole of his day – from getting up to going to bed. Invite the pupil to describe feelings as well as events. (10 minutes)

b In self-selected pairs or threes, pupils talk about their ideas. Wide-ranging discussion should be encouraged, as the next phase of the activity will benefit from a free exchange of contrasting and similar views. (10 minutes)

c Invite pupils to share any of their ideas with the class. (3–4 minutes)

d Suggest that in the future the pair or group may wish to spend the day together. Given this situation, members describe their perfect day, from the time they meet in the morning until they return to their own homes in the evening.

In groups where pupils are not close friends the need to accommodate and respond to the wishes of others is particularly challenging. (15 minutes)

e Groups which finish ahead of the others may combine to describe their perfect day.

f Inquire whether or not any group proposes to take steps so that its perfect day takes place.

Prompts for reflection

- I was surprised to learn that . . .
- The greatest difficulty our group had in deciding upon a perfect day was . . .
- The best day in my life was . . .
- I think that the idea of a perfect day is . . .
- A perfect day can only happen if . . .
- There is no such thing as a perfect day because . . .

Suggestions for follow-up work

1 Invite groups within the class to collect cuttings from local and national newspapers which they consider depict 'A perfect day'.

The pupils should put themselves 'in the shoes' of the subject(s) of the item and consider if he/they would also see the event as 'perfect'. If so, the cutting could be included as a contribution to the group's wall display.

2 Experiences viewed with hindsight are often 'rosier' than our current lives. Invite each pupil to ask an older relative or neighbour to recall some details about a perfect day. It may be of particular interest to ask the relative about the times when he was of a similar age to the pupil.

12.3 Certainty

It has been said that only one thing is certain: that nothing is certain! However, even though the course of our lives is ultimately unpredictable there are a number of events and situations which we may anticipate. Personal experience equips us with the capacity to generalise and helps us to face new situations through reference to earlier ones.

In this activity, pupils focus upon an event that many of them will experience in less than five years time – leaving school. They are asked to consider their first year out of school and to record statements about which they feel varying degrees of certainty.

Although this projection may be a fantasy it is, nevertheless, important, since the achievement of ambitions may need careful planning and sustained commitment throughout a pupil's school career. If a pupil suddenly decides to work hard in the final year at school, it may be too late to improve his performance in public examinations.

There are, of course, events over which a young person has no immediate control, for example, issues related to national political policy. Such factors may convince the young person that he is a victim of circumstances beyond his control. However, there are areas of life where the individual *can* take action, or develop the capacity to do so. We must dispel the feeling of helplessness engendered by belief in 'good luck' and 'chance', in favour of self-empowerment, which liberates the individual to be proactive and responsible.

The daily barrage of doom and despondency to which we are subjected by the media can overwhelm some young people. To emancipate them from this gloom, we should encourage pupils to realise that they *do* have the potential to influence the future and that they are not merely 'pawns' in a much bigger game.

Objectives

- to identify events or situations that are likely to occur within the first year of leaving school
- to consider what degree of certainty we may reasonably anticipate in life

Materials

Pencils
A copy of the *Probabilities sheet* (page 337) for each pupil

Procedure

a Give each pupil a *Probabilities sheet* and a pencil. Ask them to think about the likelihood of the occurrence of certain future events when they leave school. Pupils should frame statements which relate to events or situations within one year of leaving school.

b Using the sentence stem 'When I leave school I will . . .' at the top of the sheet, each pupil privately completes the sentence, writing his responses in the appropriate area on the form. If he is confident that the event will definitely occur, he writes his sentence in the *certain* area; if it is *almost certain* to occur or *maybe* will occur, he uses the appropriate categories. (10 minutes)

    Some pupils may claim that they have no idea. In this case, you could offer some prompts in terms of employment, home circumstances, leisure pursuits, living in the same area, opportunities and relationships . . .

c In groups of four, pupils discuss the contents of each category comparing and contrasting their responses. It might be helpful to suggest that they focus upon one category for a fixed period, then comment as a class, before examining the other two categories in a similar way.

d Within each group, members consider what degree of certainty they may anticipate in their lives.

Prompts for reflection

- Nothing is certain in life because . . .
- I feel certain that . . .
- As a group, members could not agree about . . .
- I thought this exercise was . . .
- At this stage, I need to prepare for leaving school by . . .

Suggestions for follow-up work

1 Ask pupils to look at magazines and newspapers and identify advertisements which promise security for individuals or their families, eg those of insurance companies. Pupils could attempt to re-design the advertisement in order to project a contrary message.
2 You could invite a member of the mathematics department to demonstrate that 'there is no such thing as a certainty'. This demonstration may lead to a discussion relating to taking risks, for example, as a gambler or a road user.

Probabilities sheet

CHOICES

When I leave school, I will . . . . . .

MAYBE

ALMOST CERTAIN

CERTAIN

12.4 Double your age

This activity invites pupils to consider the likely changes in their personal circumstances, the local environment and the national scene by the time they reach their twenties.

During the period between mid-teens and mid-twenties many people move from a high level of dependence upon their immediate family to a state of relative independence. The 'freedom' which young people believe they will achieve in becoming adult may, in reality, be an illusion. Young people's perceptions of adulthood provide the substance for their work here; you should resist the temptation to intervene in order to offer a 'grown-up' perspective.

There are three interrelated aspects within the activity; the self, the locality and the national scene. However you may wish to focus on only one. For example, the tasks relating to the local situation may feature in a lesson as part of an environmental studies course.

As with other activities, the process can be adapted not only for facets of personal and social education but for the more traditional subject areas within the curriculum.

Objectives

- to engage pupils in 'crystal-ball gazing' with reference to their personal circumstances, their local community and the national scene
- to identify those circumstances which are likely to affect all group members in an identified year

Materials

A copy of *Double your age* (page 400) for each pupil
A copy of *Our world* (page 401) for each group of four pupils (ideally this should be a different colour from the individual pupil's sheet)
Pencils

Procedure

a Give each pupil a copy of the *Double your age sheet* and a pencil. Ask the pupil to double his present age to arrive at a particular year in the future. He then writes this year under each of the three headings.

b As a private exercise, the pupil writes a statement in each of the four boxes in column 1, which refers to *Me in the year* . . . , indicating what he thinks will be happening then. (5 minutes)

c Pupils form groups of four according to the year they arrived at. Hand out the *Our world sheet*. In groups, pupils discuss their statements. In column 1, *Us in the year* . . . the group records four statements relating to their personal circumstances in the identified year, on which all members agree. (5–7 minutes)

d Pupils remain in their groups but undertake the next phase of the activity independently. Each person writes a statement in each of the four boxes in column 2 about 'My city, town or village in the year . . . '. Ask the pupils to identify differences between the present day and their year of the future. (5 minutes)

e In groups, pupils discuss their statements and in column 2 of *Our World* they record four commonly held views about their locality in the future. Within any group, there may be pupils who live in different settings; they should try to search for common elements even though the environments may differ considerably. (5–10 minutes)

f If time permits, the third column *This country in the year* . . . should be completed and discussed as outlined above. (15 minutes)

Prompts for reflection

- We found it difficult to agree about . . .
- I think the greatest difference between my situation today and in the stated year is likely to be . . .
- The biggest change in the local environment will be . . .
- The great difference between this country now and in the stated year is likely to be . . .

Suggestions for follow-up work

Invite pupils to interview people they know who are in their twenties to find out how their present circumstances differ from or correspond to their hopes and predictions when they were the same age as the interviewer. The interview schedule will need to be carefully prepared to ensure that questions do not cause offence. It will be illuminating for pupils to ascertain, where possible, why aspirations were or were not realised.

CHOICES

Double your age

1 Me in the Year	2 My city, town or village in the Year	3 This country in the Year . . . .

Our world

1 Us in the Year	2 Our city, town or village in the Year	3 This country in the Year . . . . .

12.5 Predictions

Many newspapers and magazines carry regular features relating to predictions, for example, horse racing forecasts and horoscopes. Indeed, predictions are to be found in everyday conversation with such expressions as 'I bet you that . . . ' and 'I reckon . . . '.

This activity uses the technique of 'standpoint-taking', where pupils are asked to adopt one of four positions in response to a given prediction and to justify their opinion to someone who has taken a different stance.

Through the use of reasoned argument, one may hope to persuade one's partner but equally one should be open-minded and be willing to be convinced. The exercise is likely to reveal extreme positions of intransigence and submission, as well as compromise through negotiation.

Pupils are required to 'think on their feet' without reference to any other source. However, some pupils may hesitate to make a decision until they have noted the intentions of their friend(s). This issue regarding peer pressure may be considered as it arises or deferred to a later date. Alternatively, you might ask each pupil to make a written commitment as to the decision he has taken, so that he is not influenced by peers.

Objectives

- to examine the likelihood of predicted events actually happening
- to develop reasoned arguments in support of or against certain predictions

Materials

A blank postcard for each pupil
Pencils

Procedure

a All chairs should be placed against the walls to enable unhindered movement around the room.

b Explain that four corners of the room have a particular significance in this activity. Each represents a standpoint: 'strongly agree', 'agree', 'strongly disagree' or 'disagree' (see Figure 12.a)

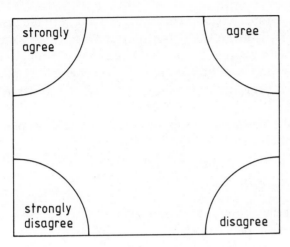

Fig. 12.a

Labels showing these standpoints may be fixed to the wall in each corner.

c Explain that pupils will be invited to complete a statement which begins 'By the year 2001 . . . '. The statement will be read out to the group. For each statement the pupil should stand in the corner which corresponds most closely to his viewpoint.

Give one or more of the examples below to ensure that the pupils are clear about the procedure.

Examples

By the year 2001 . . .

. . . a cure for cancer will have been discovered

. . . smoking will have been banned in all shops

. . . all pensioners will be given a free TV licence

. . . there will be a major peace agreement between USA and USSR

. . . people will live happily together in all our cities

. . . the rivers of England will have no fish

d Give each pupil a blank postcard on which to write one completed sentence 'By the year 2001 . . . '.

No pupil should be pressurised to produce an example. If the pupils do not generate any issues, you could use the issues given in c. (5 minutes)

e Collect all the cards and number them at random.

f Ask for a volunteer to pick a number within the range of cards (or select a particular card yourself). Read out the statement on the card and ask each pupil to take up a position in one of the four corners.

g Ask who wrote the card. The writer, having seen the distribution of the pupils, is given the opportunity to say which 'corner' should discuss with another 'corner', for example, 'strongly agree' with 'disagree' and 'strongly disagree' with 'agree'. Pupils from the chosen corners find a partner and discuss the differences in their viewpoints.

h Repeat the procedure using different cards and people, for as long as pupils wish to continue.

Prompts for reflection

• I think I have changed my views about . . .
• I feel certain that I am right about . . .
• I was surprised that so many people felt . . .
• I was surprised that so few people felt . . .
• I think the most likely prediction to come true is . . .

Suggestions for follow-up work

1 Some magazines and newspapers contain horoscopes which the pupils may wish to investigate, finding out by whom and how they are written. A comparison across a number of publications may reveal some interesting features about horoscopes.

2 Invite groups to check on the extent to which published predictions have come true. Back numbers of *Old Moore's Almanac* may prove useful.

12.6 Life chances

The situation presented is designed to illustrate how unpredictable occurrences can disrupt even the best-laid plans. Through role play, the pupils attempt to assess and respond to certain events.

It is difficult to prepare young people for the harsh realities of life. However, role play and simulation may help them consider a range of coping strategies. 'Learning by doing' is preferable in considering how to cope in a given situation rather than being 'told what to do if . . .'. How to develop the inner resources to cope with our own problems and those of other people should be high on the agenda of any personal and social education programme and should be a recurrent theme throughout an individual's school career.

Objectives

- to assess the impact of unpredictable events in our lives
- to consider how we deal with stressful situations

Materials

A copy of the *Personal Information sheet* (page 347) for each pupil
Sufficient copies of the *Events cards* (page 348) to ensure that at least two pupils have the same card in each case
Pencils

Procedure

a Issue pupils with the *Personal information sheet*. Ask each pupil to read the sheet and assume the role of the person described. The pupil should extend the role so that he has the feeling of 'becoming' this person.
b Explain that each person will receive information of an event that has recently happened to him. Give each pupil one of the ten *Events cards* on a random basis. (Each event must be allocated to at least two people, therefore not all cards may be used in a small class.) Ask the pupil to consider what impact this event will have upon his life. (The pupil is not required to write down any information.) (3 minutes)

c The pupil finds a partner(s) who has considered the same event and they discuss their views. (3–5 minutes)

d Without further discussion beyond the groups, give each pupil another event and ask him once again to consider its impact upon his life.

e Pupils find (new) partners and discuss their views.

f You may wish to repeat this task several more times, depending upon the time available and any adaptation made to the suggested procedure.

g For the final ten minutes of the session, pupils form self-selected groups in order to discuss how they would cope with one or two of these unpredictable events. You could identify one person in each group to offer one of his events as an issue for discussion. Other pupils in the group should de-role and become 'friends' who may wish to provide comfort, guidance and support.

h Invite a group to share its discussion with the class. All remaining pupils de-role and offer their views.

Prompts for reflection

● The event which I most fear happening to me is . . .
● I sometimes wonder how I would cope if . . .
● Even though I would be upset, I think I could cope if . . .
● The greatest event in my life so far was when . . .
● My greatest ambition is . . .

Suggestions for follow-up work

Invite pupils to write details of three unpredictable events which they think may happen in their lives within the next five years. Collect the contributions and ensure that any issues likely to cause distress to any pupil are removed. Transcribe the remainder on to individual cards.

In each group of three, give each person a different card. In turn, members present the event and describe what impact it might have on their lives. The other two pupils offer advice, guidance and support as they see fit.

Before the next person in the group offers his scenario, check that the first pupil is satisfied with the attention he has received from his peers. Continue until all three pupils have received help from each other.

Personal information

I am nineteen years old. I . . .

. . . play badminton for a local club on Wednesdays.

. . . work in a bar on Friday and Saturday evenings.

. . . have recently passed my driving test.

. . . own a 'W' registration car.

. . . work as a machine operator in a local factory.

. . . live with my parents.

. . . live twenty miles from my fiancé(e).

. . . keep all my savings at home.

. . . am going abroad on holiday next week.

. . . plan to get married in a month's time

Event cards

1 I break both legs in a road accident.

2 I win £200,000 on the Football Pools.

3 A distant relative dies and leaves me £550.

4 I have an operation to remove my appendix.

5 My home is completely destroyed by fire.

6 An uncle buys me a sports car.

7 I decide to run a youth club five nights of the week.

8 My fiancé(e) becomes seriously ill.

9 I am offered a well-paid job abroad.

10 I lose my job because my firm closes.

12.7 High hopes

From early childhood, young people talk about their ambitions and aspirations. Over time, due to changing personal and social circumstances new insights are gained and fresh perspectives adopted.

In this activity, a questionnaire is used to help pupils focus on four interrelated areas of their lives:

- environment
- 'new' relationships
- possessions
- responsibilities towards others

For some of the issues raised in the questionnaire the pupil may say that he has 'never really thought about it'. If so, you will need to decide whether to persuade or help the young person to arrive at a provisional or tentative response, or to suggest that he leaves the statement uncompleted.

There may be pupils who see little hope for their future or that of the world. Support is vitally important for such young people, not just to help them complete the required task but over a sustained period of time. Daily experience of conflict and turmoil in life may do little to promote positive self-esteem or generate feelings of optimism. You may need to create a classroom climate which makes pupils feel that life is precious and worth living and to emphasise that we do have the ability to create opportunities for ourselves even against seemingly insuperable odds. To illustrate this point, you could quote one or two examples of people who have achieved their ambitions in spite of earlier failure or rejection.

Objectives

- to ascertain what common and unique ambitions and aspirations are prevalent within a peer group
- to develop listening skills

Materials

One *When I am 21 sheet* (page 352)
Pencils

Procedure

a Hand out the *When I am 21 sheets*, and ask each pupil to complete the questions as a private exercise. There is an opportunity for additional statements to be added at the end of the sheet. Explain that the details given will provide the basis of an agenda for the discussion of ambitions and aspirations with a partner.

b Pupils form self-selected pairs, and choose who will be **A** and **B**. Pupil **A** presents his details while **B** listens and does not interrupt. (3–5 minutes)

c Pupil **B** presents his details and **A** listens. (The teacher may adjust the time allocated, depending upon how much the pupils need.)

d Ask each pupil to check with his partner which details he would not wish to be shared with another pair. (This will reduce the likelihood of anger or embarrassment arising as a result of personal disclosures.)

e Two pairs join together. One of the original pairs label themselves 1 and 2, the other 3 and 4.

f Pupil 1 describes what his partner (pupil 2) told him, *as if he were his partner*. He begins his presentation by saying 'My name is . . . and when I am 21, I hope to . . . '

You should act as timekeeper and judge when it is appropriate for the presentation to end. (about 2–3 minutes)

g Pupil 2 adopts the persona of pupil 1 and describes to the group what he heard *as if he were pupil 1*.

h Pupils 3 and 4 repeat the procedure.

i Each group de-roles to discuss shared and different ambitions and aspirations for the future.

Prompts for reflection

- I was surprised to learn that . . .
- We shared similar feelings about . . .
- I felt the exercise helped us to . . .
- The best part of the exercise was when . . .
- I found that my ability to listen was . . .

Suggestions for follow-up work

1 Invite pupils to write an employer's reference for themselves at the age of 21, based on the results of their questionnaire and their discussions with their peers. You could negotiate with groups, in advance, the particular jobs they might think of.
2 Some pupils may wish to write an advertisement (no more than 25 words) offering their services to local employers. They should imagine that they are themselves at 21 years of age.

When I am 21

CHOICES

Please tick only *one* box in *each numbered section.*

When I am 21, I hope to . . . . .

(1)		(2)	
Live abroad	☐	Live in a flat	☐
Live in this country	☐	Live in a house	☐
		Live in a maisonette	☐
		Live in a mobile home	☐

(3)		(4)	
Live in a city	☐	Be married	☐
Live in a town	☐	Be single	☐
Live in a village	☐		

(5)		(6)	
Have a child	☐	Own a car	☐
Have children	☐	Not have a car	☐
Have no children	☐		

(7)		(8)	
Work for myself	☐	Live near relatives	☐
Work for someone else	☐	Live away from relatives	☐

(For your own sentences)

When I am 21, I hope to

(9)--

(10)--

(11)--

(13)--

© 1986   David Settle/Charles Wise   Basil Blackwell

12.8 My success story

To look back on the future certainly seems to be a contradiction in terms but that is what is involved in this activity.

The pupil imagines himself as a 70-year-old and is asked to recall significant incidents which give him reason to believe that his life has been a success. To predict and review the events of early adulthood will be a demanding experience but it may encourage pupils to think about the consequences of their actions. For example, a challenge accepted today which may not exist tomorrow, may have a positive and profound effect upon career opportunities. On the other hand, an impulsive response to accept one cigarette may be the starting point of a long-term smoking habit which may well prove detrimental to health.

You need to think carefully about the long-term prospects of each of the pupils before embarking upon this activity – in some cases it might cause considerable distress and should be avoided. Like other activities in the book, knowledge of the personal circumstances of your pupils will inform your decisions as to the appropriateness of the content and context.

Objectives

- to provide pupils with an opportunity to outline those events and incidents during their adult life which they believe would be indicative of a successful life

Materials

For each pupil:
One copy of *My success story* (page 357)
A4 writing paper
Pencil
Rough paper

Procedure

a Give each pupil a copy of *My success story*, together with a sheet of lined writing paper, rough paper and a pencil.

b Read the story aloud and ask the pupils to follow the text in silence.

c Explain that each pupil should continue where the text finished in order to make his own story. Remind pupils that only key events or incidents between the age of 15 and 70 should be recorded. It may be helpful to suggest that no more than six landmarks are identified so that pupils see the writing of their story as a manageable task. Suggest that pupils spend a few minutes writing brief notes about the key points.

d Set a time limit so that there is an opportunity for those pupils who wish to read their stories to the class to do so. You need to work alongside some pupils who are experiencing difficulties.

e Invite pupils to read their stories to the class.

Prompts for reflection

- I do not think my own life will turn out this way because . . .
- The best thing that could happen to me as an adult would be . . .
- My greatest worry about the future is . . .

Suggestions for follow-up work

1 Invite each pupil to design an epitaph to attach to his story. For guidance on the brevity and style of epitaphs they might visit cathedrals, cemeteries and churches. The local library may have reference books on the subject.

2 Ask pupils to interview elderly people in order to see which landmarks give them reason to believe that their lives have been successful. If possible, pupils could tape-record the interviews as the memories are worth retaining in the school's archives. Pupils may wish to discuss the past with their grandparents and great-grandparents and keep a copy of the recording along with photographs in their family scrap book.

My success story

On my 70th birthday, I look back with pride on all that I have achieved. I have been lucky and in spite of a few unhappy incidents along the way, I feel that my life has been worthwhile.

I can remember a great deal about my childhood, but it was not until I was 15 years old that my success story really began.

What follows is a brief description of the most important landmarks in my life . . .

12.9 For the next generation

The final activity invites young people to consider what information about present-day schooling they would wish to pass on to their children. At the outset, it is important to ascertain from the pupils ways in which a record should be compiled. The activity focuses upon the production of a tape-recorded commentary on current events and experiences in the school; existing documentation such as school magazines and reports, photographs and newspaper cuttings could also be useful.

The conversion of an ordered content list into presentation form will offer a challenge to the group. Members should be encouraged to think carefully about ways of attracting and maintaining the listener's attention. The use of jingles, improvised music, interviews and sound effects may greatly enhance the quality of the recording. The group may also wish to devise a script to go with the presentation. This part of the activity will require a high level of cooperation between group members.

Objectives

• to identify the features of present-day schooling that we may wish to describe to the next generation

Materials

A tape cassette-recorder for each group, with tape
Newsprint
Thick felt-tip pens
Masking tape
A4 writing paper
Pencils

Procedure

a Divide the class into at least four groups (preferably more, if there are sufficient tapes and recorders, so the maximum size is six members).

b Set the scene for the exercise, by saying something like, 'The next generation (as earlier ones) will probably ask you as a parent or a relative "What was school like?". You may respond in a few words, but it is likely that the child will want to know a great deal more. Today, we are going to prepare a two-minute tape of your views about your present-day experience of school.'
Make sure all the pupils are clear about this setting.

c Give each group a sheet of newsprint and a felt-tip pen. Invite members to brainstorm responses to the sentence stem 'I think we should include comments about . . .'.
Point out that all responses should be recorded on the newsprint even if they represent contradictory or similar statements. (5 minutes)

d Display the newsprint on the walls so that the information is available to all groups.

e Give a sheet of paper and a pencil to each group and ask members to decide upon the content and presentation of their tape. The class should be made aware of the time limit of this task; time checks should be provided at various intervals. (10–15 minutes)

f Distribute tape-recorders and tapes. Groups may need to work in different areas if mains electricity supplies are limited in one room. Having an area to themselves may also help a group to feel less inhibited.

g Groups work together to create a prototype of their presentation. Encourage them to use extra 'aids', (music, script etc) in the presentation. (15 minutes)

h The group which finishes ahead of others should take the opportunity to produce a more polished performance.

i Each group presents its recording to the class.

Prompts for reflection

• The most difficult part of the exercise was . . .
• As a group, members disagreed about . . .
• I think that this activity was . . .
• There were occasions when I felt . . .
• I think the most interesting thing on our tape was . . .
• I think my children will be most interested to hear about . . .

Suggestions for follow-up work

1 Invite pupils to consider other media that may be used to convey feelings about schooling to the next generation, eg artwork, poetry and songs.
2 Some pupils could do research in the school and public libraries to compile a collection of poems and prose which refer to impressions and memories of schooling.
3 Interviews with elderly people will provide an interesting insight into schooling 50 years ago. They may be able to provide photographs, school magazines and reports, newspaper cuttings, badges and other artefacts.
4 Invite each group to consider which *ten* artefacts it would wish to preserve in order to convey an impression of contemporary life to their grandchildren. (Only one book or video-cassette may be included in the collection.)

Sources for related teaching materials

The following organisations either produce teaching materials or will be able to advise on further sources.

Age Concern
60 Pitcairn Road
Mitcham
Surrey
CR4 3LL
Tel: 01 640 5431

British Nutrition Foundation
15 Belgrave Square
London
SW1X 8PS
Tel: 01 235 4904

Careers Research and Advisory Centre (CRAC)
Bateman Street
Cambridge
CB2 1LZ
Tel: 0223 354551

Commission for Racial Equality
Eliot House,
Allington Street
London
SW1 5EH
Tel: 01 828 7022

Community Service Volunteers
237 Pentonville Road
London
N1 9NJ
Tel: 01 278 6601

Consumers' Association
14 Buckingham Street
London
WC2
Tel: 01 839 1222

Development Education Centre
Gillett Centre
Selly Oak Colleges
Birmingham
B29 6LE
Tel: 021 472 3255

Equal Opportunities Commission
Overseas House
Quay Street
Manchester
M3 3HN
Tel: 061 833 9244

Health Education Council
78 New Oxford Street
London
WC1A 1AH
Tel: 01 631 0930

Help the Aged
1–7 Sekforde Street
London
EC1R 0BE
Tel: 01 253 0253

ILEA Learning Resources Branch
Thackeray Road
London
SW8 3TB
Tel: 01 622 9966

Lifeskills Associates
Clarendon Chambers
51 Clarendon Road
Leeds
LS2 9NZ
Tel: 0532 467128

Mind (National Association for Mental Health)
22 Harley Street
London
W1N 2ED
Tel: 01 637 0741

National Children's Bureau
8 Wakeley Street
London
EC1V 7QE
Tel: 01 278 9441–7

National Council for Civil Liberties
21 Tabard Street
London
SE1 4LA
Tel: 01 403 3888

NSPCC
1 Riding House Street
London
W1P 8AA
Tel: 01 580 8812

Open University
Learning Materials Service
P.O. Box 188
Milton Keynes
MK7 6DH
Tel: 0908 566744

Oxfam
274 Banbury Road
Oxford
OX2 7DZ
Tel: 0865 56777

Royal Society for the Prevention of Accidents (ROSPA)
Cannon House
Priory Queensway
Birmingham
B4 6BS
Tel: 021 233 2461

Save the Children Fund
Mary Datchelor House
17 Grove Lane
London
SE5 8RD
Tel: 01 703 5400

Shelter
157 Waterloo Road
London
SE1 8UU
Tel: 01 633 9377

Spastics Society
12 Park Crescent
London
W1N 4EQ
Tel: 01 636 5020

Teachers Advisory Council on Alcohol and Drug Education (TACADE)
3rd Floor
Furness House
Trafford Road
Salford
M5 2XJ
Tel: 061 848 0351/2

The Children's Society
Old Town Hall
Kennington Road
London
SE11 4QD
Tel: 01 735 2441

War on Want
1 London Bridge Street
London
SE1 9SG
Tel: 01 403 2266

Your local Citizen's Advice Bureau, Community Relations Office, and the Advisory Service of your Area Health Authority and Local Education Authority will be able to provide further information of local, regional and national organisations.

Useful Reference Books

Brandes, D and Philips, H *Gamesters Handbook* Book 1. London: Hutchinson, 1981.

Brandes, D *Gamesters Handbook* Two. London: Hutchinson, 1982.

Brandes, D and Ginnis, P *A Guide to Student-centred Learning* Oxford: Blackwell, 1986.

Bulman, L and Jenkins, D *The Pastoral Curriculum* Oxford: Blackwell, 1986.

Butler, B and Elliott, D *Teaching and Learning for Practice* Aldershot: Gower Publishing Co, 1985.

Butterworth, C and MacDonald, M *Teaching Social Education and Communication: a Practical Handbook* London: Hutchinson, 1985.

Button, L *Group Tutoring for the Form Teacher* Books 1 and 2. London: Hodder & Stoughton, 1982.

Clanfield, J and Wells, H C *100 Ways to Enhance Self-concept in the Classroom* Englewood Cliffs, NJ: Prentice-Hall, 1976.

Cleaton, D R *Exercises in Social and Personal Education* Richmond: Careers Consultants Ltd, 1985.

David, K *Personal and Social Education in Secondary Schools* London: Longman for Schools Council, 1983.

Davies, G T *A First Year Tutorial Handbook* Oxford: Blackwell, 1986.

Ellis, D and Whittington, D *New Directions in Social Skill Training* Beckenham: Croom Helm, 1982.

Foster, J *Lifelines: a Social and Personal Development Course* (5 books) Glasgow: Collins, 1985.

Hamblin, D *Teaching Study Skills* Oxford: Blackwell, 1981.

Hamblin, D *Pastoral Care: a Training Manual* Oxford: Blackwell, 1984.

Hamblin, D *A Pastoral Programme* Oxford: Blackwell, 1986.

Hopson, B *Lifeskills Teaching* Maidenhead: McGraw Hill, 1981.

Hopson, B and Scally, M *Lifeskills Teaching Programmes* (Numbers 1, 2 & 3) Leeds: Lifeskills Associates, 1980.

Hopson, B and Scally, M *Build Your Own Rainbow* Leeds: Lifeskills Associates, 1984.

Hunt, S and Hilton, J *Individual Development and Social Experience* Hemel Hempstead: George Allen and Unwin, 1975.

Lancashire County Council *Active Tutorial Work* (6 books) Oxford: Blackwell, 1978.

McPhail, P, Ungoed-Thomas, J and Chapman, H *Moral Education in the Secondary School* York: Longman for Schools Council, 1972.

Morgan, J *Tutor Group Worksheets* Oxford: Blackwell, (Year 1, 2, 3 & 4), 1985.

Priestley, P *et al Social Skills and Personal Problem-solving* London: Tavistock, 1978.

Pring, R *Personal and Social Education in the Curriculum* London: Hodder and Stoughton, 1984.

Rennie, J, Lunzer, G A *et al Social Education: an Experiment in Four Secondary Schools* (Schools Council Working Paper 51) Evans/Methuen Educational, 1974.

Rice, W *Informal Methods in Health and Social Education* Manchester: TACADE, 1981.

Singer, E and Johnson, R *Personal Development: a Personal Effectiveness Resource Pack* Sheffield: COIC, 1985.

Stradling, R, Noctor, M and Baines, B *Teaching Controversial Issues* London: Arnold

Thacker, J *Steps to Success: an Interpersonal Problem-solving Approach for Children* Windsor: NFER-Nelson, 1982.

Wakeman, B *Personal, Social and Moral Education* Tring: Lion Publishing, 1984.